W9-BVA-937

ROCKS & MINERALS

Triune Books

ROCKS & MINERALS

by Cedric Rogers

Acknowledgments

All the illustrations in this book were photographed by Geremy Butler, apart from those credited below to Bennett's of Cambourne, Dr Richard W. Braithwaite, the Department of the Environment, the Geological Survey, Axel Poignant, UP International and the author (95*b* only).

The specimens and engravings illustrated in this book are reproduced by kind permission of the author: 8*l*, 10, 11*b*, 15, 19, 39, 42*t*, 42*b*, 43*t*, 43*b*, 45*b*, 46, 47, 48*t*, 48*b*, 50*tl*, 50*tr*, 55*rc*, 55*b*, 62, 63, 64, 65*tl*, 65*tr*, 65*b*, 66, 67*t*, 67*b*, 68*l*, 68*r*, 69*t*, 69*b*, 70, 71*tl*, 71*bl*, 71*br*, 72, 73*t*, 73*b*, 74*tl*, 74*tr*, 74*bl*, 76, 77*tl*, 77*tr*, 78, 79*tl*, 79*tr*, 80*r*, 82, 83*t*, 86*tl*, 86*tr*, 87*t*, 87*bl*, 87*br*, 88, 89*b*, 90*l*, 90*r*, 91(*all*), 93, 95*tl*, 95*tr*, 95*b*, 96, 97(*all*), 98, 99(*all*), 100(*all*), 101*t*, 101*b*, 102, 103(*all*), 104, 105, 106, 107(*all*), 112*t*, 112*bl*, 113*t*, 113*b*, 114(*all*), 115, 123, 133*b*, 134, 138*tr*, 138*bl*, 138*br*, 139(*all*); Bennett's of Cambourne, Cornwall: 119; Dr Richard W. Braithwaite, University of Manchester: 1, 49*b*, 92*t*, 92*b*, 140(*all*), 141*t*, 141*b*; the Trustees of the British Museum (Natural History): 17, 20, 21, 23, 24, 25, 26, 27*tr*, 28, 29, 30, 31, 32, 33, 34, 35, 36, 41, 49, 51*t*, 52, 53, 54*lc*, 56, 57, 60, 61, 71*tr*, 74*br*, 75, 77*b*, 79*b*, 80*l*, 83*b*, 84, 85, 86*b*; Luisa Clark: 8*r*; the Department of the Environment: 18; C. M. Dixon, 37*t*, 37*b*, 38, 111*t*, 111*b*, 116*t*, 116*b*, 117*t*, 117*b*; the Geological Survey: 11*t*, 12, 13, 35, 55, 108, 109, 110, 118; Gregory, Bottley & Co: 7, 64, 81, 89*t*, 132, 144; Axel Poignant: 14, 22, 27*tl*, 27*b*, 124; United Press International: 9; Geoffrey Van Ltd Mineral Gallery, London: 128; Thomas Yoseloff, New York, 121.

The diagrams on pages 58, 59 and 81 were drawn by Clive Crook

The publishers gratefully acknowledge the help and facilities for photography provided by the staff of the Mineral Gallery and Library of the Natural History Museum, London and by Messrs Gregory, Bottley & Co and Messrs Geoffrey Van Ltd.

ISBN 0 85674 010 1
Published by
Triune Books, London, England
© Trewin Copplestone Publishing Ltd 1973
Printed in Spain
By Printer, Industria Gráfica S.A. Tuset 19
Barcelona, San Vicente dels Horts 1973
Depósito legal B. 14790-1973
Mohn Gordon Ltd. London

Page 1 *An aragonite crystal from Cumberland, England, photographed through a microscopic lens*

Page 3 *Rosettes of barite on a septarian nodule, broken open, from the Isle of Sheppey, England*

Contents   Page

Preface

The purpose of this book is to whet some appetites which can only be assauged by further study and personal experience. If one does not have the makings of a mineral collector, or 'rockhound', there is nothing much to be done about it. But it is only too easy for one who has, to allow opportunity to pass him by—or perhaps not recognise opportunity when it is there. One thing which often frightens off likely enthusiasts is the apparent technicality and even dryness of the subject. One is almost immediately confronted by a host of outlandish and unpronounceable names which seem to be based on no system whatever. Actually, if you stop to consider this, you realize that any natural history subject is likely to present a similar problem. Gardeners are far worse off in the tongue-twisting stakes.

Mineralogy is a study which claims adherents from a very wide range of occupations, and the dividing line between amateur and professional is obscure. In fact, the truly professional mineralogist is comparatively rare, and much of the research work is done by people whose work embraces mineralogy, such as chemists and geologists. It is a subject which for some can become so obsessive that almost involuntarily they find they are classing themselves out of their amateur status.

For the newcomer, there seems to be so much to learn before you can even get started. The obvious way to overcome this (unless you have already been introduced to the subject at school, or through enthusiastic friends) is to join a club. This is the quickest, most effective and for many the most agreeable way to embark on any hobby, assuming there is a club available.

On the other hand there are those who are natural loners and shy away from clubs. For either kind, I hope to give some guidance, and also for those who would simply like to browse among the pictures and perhaps be prompted to look for the odd specimen to buy and enjoy as an ornament.

If you go into any fisherman's den, you are likely to see the notice 'Beware of Fish Pox'. I must admit that when (before becoming infected) I first saw the one saying 'Beware of Rock Pox', it seemed a bit far fetched—it is not. The virus of the fever which sends men off into desolate corners of the earth, their burros laden with picks and shovels, spurred on with dreams of treasure in 'them thar hills' must be lurking in most of us. There is no doubt in my mind that for every confirmed rockhound there are ten potential converts.

It should be mentioned here that although the emphasis so far has been on the active mineral collector who goes out into the field, and whose chief pleasure is to find his own specimens, there is another side of collecting to be covered. Many people do not have the opportunity to do their own collecting, others may aspire to finer and more varied specimens than they are likely to pick up for themselves. There are the connoisseurs who can spend considerable sums of money (using what Americans call the Silver Pick) building up a significant collection and who may be compared to antique collectors—after all, mineral specimens are the oldest antiques of all—and who rely largely on dealers, auctions and the occasional lucky find in some forgotten attic. Today good specimens are even bought as investments—as are works of art. Although connoisseur collecting has a long and honourable history (the rockhound, as understood today, is a fairly modern phenomenon), there has been comparatively little written about it. I hope to deal with this aspect more fully than is usual, particularly as many people combine both.

Mineral collecting as an adjunct to the allied hobby of lapidary work will be touched upon, and gemstones, in as much as they are rocks or minerals, will be dealt with as such. I know from personal experience that dreams of finding gold and rubies, diamonds and emeralds, were the spur that set the hobbyhorse in motion for me—and I am sure I am not alone here. Witness the number of books on minerals which contain 'gemstone' in the title, although true gems may only occupy a few pages altogether.

But if gems were the spur, the prize turned out to be mineral specimens, which to the uninitiated might be interesting but otherwise worthless. Often, in fact, the pieces of stone that may be treasures to a diehard rockhound do not even look interesting!

*Some interesting corners of a world-famous rock
shop in London. Established in the heyday of
Victorian mineral-collecting about 1850, it is still
going strong.* **Top** *The inverted glass jars contain
water-soluble minerals, such as halite, to protect
them from atmospheric moisture.* **Above** *A rock-
splitting vice.*
Overleaf *Calcite-lined geodes from Mexico. The one
on the left shows two formations: a chunky crystal
and a platy mass.*

My own infection came about through a series of circumstances. Clearly I had never been exposed to the bug before since it turned out that I had no resistance whatever. It started with an unscheduled visit to the American Museum of Natural History in New York at a time when I was living in Pennsylvania, making a livelihood at portrait painting. I had gone to the museum with the immediate intention of finding out something about the geology of the area in which I was living. I had been painting some landscapes and the idea occurred that a knowledge of landscape's 'anatomy' might be as valuable as the knowledge of human anatomy is for painting people. As it turned out, the geology gallery was closed for alterations, but the mineral gallery was very much open.

As a consolation prize the rest of the afternoon was spent taking in dazzling displays of gem-stones, crystals and other gorgeous looking minerals. Even then the penny didn't drop, that one could become personally involved in anything which seemed as remote from everyday life as these. But just as a fossil hunter can be happy with pieces of ammonite here and a scrap of trilobite there without needing to own a whole set of brontosaurus bones, so one discovers that it isn't necessary to find the Koh-i-noor diamond to enjoy building up a mineral collection. This discovery was to come gradually.

It started in the museum shop, where I discovered a cheerful and unpretentious field guide to collecting minerals and gems in the New York area. I did not have to be told what topaz, garnet and carnelian were, although some of the other names were pretty daunting. What was one to make of 'phlogopite' or 'leucophœnicite' for instance? But the light hearted text and amusing maps quickly dispelled any idea that this was a matter only for fossilised greybeards with astronomical IQ's.

When I returned to England a few years later, I was well and truly hooked. In fact, the area which chose itself as the next port of call was the for me irresistible combination of an artists' colony with its site in the middle of the most richly mineralised area of Britain—Cornwall. On arrival, one of the first things I set out to do was to try to dig out all the available literature, and particularly anything on the lines of the guide which had started the whole thing. The literature turned out to consist mostly of rather obstruse snippets tucked away here and there in the pamphlets, proceedings and transactions of various societies. There was nothing for the amateur at all. The only answer was to gather it all together and write my own. This done, a new career imposed itself on one whose allegiances had always been torn between the arts and the sciences.

In the case of this book, the aim is both simpler and broader. If I can in any way communicate some of the pleasure and even excitement that the study and pursuit of minerals have given me, so much the better. If not, the pictures are sure to succeed where I have failed.

There are so many excellent books now on the market giving the technical details necessary for a more complete understanding, that it is pointless to duplicate them here. I have aimed at covering new ground as far as possible and at filling in gaps in the literature, as well as at giving as much fundamental information as seems required for getting launched on the hobby, whether you intend to collect with hammer and chisel, or chequebook, or both. And if your interest is a passive one of reading, studying pictures and museum collections, start right here.

Introduction to minerals

The science of the earth's structure is geology, as is well known. Rocks are the stuff that geologists deal with. But what are rocks made of? The answer is minerals, the stuff that mineralogists are concerned with.

One sometimes gets the impression that geologists and mineralogists each regard the other as unspeakable oafs. This must be a false impression, because the two fields are so intermingled that it is difficult to imagine one without the other. A geologist, if he is to understand his subject, must have some knowledge of the natural chemicals his rocks are made of, while the mineralogist must have at least a smattering of geological types and formations before he can start looking for the minerals he wants, because there is a vital connection here.

It might be said that the relation between mineralogy and geology is the same as between chemistry and physics. Mineralogy and chemistry deal with basic substances, their molecular structure, how they happen, how they can be changed and to what use they can be put. Physics and geology are about mass and energy, time and space. Geology is also indirectly concerned with the science of biology, because fossils, plants and animals are the key to geological time. Bridging the gap is the petrologist, whose chief concern is what rocks are made of and how.

However, there are times when it seems that a geologist is unaware of the existence of minerals, and *vice versa*. Ask a mineralogist to describe a geologist and the answer might be 'someone who will stand on a bunch of calcite crystals in order to reach a fossil fish-bone'. This is a slander on most geologists. But it is a fact that one can read a geologist's account of a certain location rich in minerals that will go into great detail about the synclines and anticlines, faults and unconformities, mention the occurrence of some obscure fossil and comment on the lack of others, but not mention a word about the large pieces of fluorite he kept tripping over. To be fair, a mineralogist's account of a field trip is likely to be just as single-minded.

Old-timers operating a sluice at a Dawson City gold mine, Canada.

Anyone who has played the game 'twenty questions' knows that a mineral is something which is not animal or vegetable, or derived from either. This is putting things rather back to front, as all matter starts off as mineral. Plants convert minerals in the soil into the organic matter which animals feed on. A more exact definition of 'mineral' will follow in the next chapter. Suffice to say, at this point, that we will be most concerned with minerals as attractive or interesting specimens which can be acquired for a collection (or for some other use, such as material for making gems). Rocks and their geological setting will be considered only in so far as they provide a background to the study of minerals.

The appeal of a mineral can be in its colour, its shape and its lustre (how it reflects light). These are also important factors in identifying them. Gemstones are, with the exception of pearl and coral (animal), jet and amber (vegetable), all part of the mineral kingdom, which in this case includes rock. The distinction between rock and mineral will be dealt with in the chapter.

It is through gems and precious metals that many of us become aware of minerals as an end rather than a means. Tracing the history of man and the mineral world, one finds on the one hand that stone, particularly flint, and later various metals, provided him with most of his tools. But at the same time, these very minerals, particularly the more attractive ones, were incorporated in his life as ornaments and fetishes. The myths and superstitions connected with stones have roots in the earliest human cultures.

Legends and fairy stories abound with references to magic stones, and the association of various gemstones to the zodiac and other mystical concepts is an ancient one. The popularity of birthstones as a means of personal identification with a piece of jewellery has prompted all kinds of similar associations with hours of the day, days of the week, wedding anniversaries, significance in dreams, countries, apostles and guardian angels, which may not have very deep roots in the past, but must be very stimulating for the gem trade.

The poets have found minerals of all kinds to be a source of vivid imagery. The euphony of many of the names, is self-evident, particularly those of the gem minerals, which also evoke a rich array of glowing colour – malachite, zircon, turquoise, sardonyx and lapis lazuli, which bring to mind the stately Spanish galleon in John Masefield's 'Cargoes':

With a cargo of diamonds,
emeralds, amethysts, topazes,
and cinnamon, and gold moidores.

The ancient Jews in their wanderings over the Sinai desert developed a preoccupation with stones which is reflected in the Bible – the symbolism of the Rock, the stones that speak, the pillars of salt, the twelve gems of the high priest's breast plate: sard, topaz, carbuncle (garnet), emerald, sapphire, diamond, 'ligure', agate, amethyst, beryl, onyx, and and jasper, in the book of Exodus (presumed to be the origin of the idea of birthstones).

I have vivid recollections of a somewhat fidgety choirboy listening to a lay reader reciting passages from Revelations, larded with references to gold and iron, silver and stone. But when he came to intoning the awesome names of the foundation stones of the Holy City – Jasper, Sapphire, Chalcedony, Emerald, Sardonyx, Sardius, Chrysolite, Beryl, Topaz, Chrysoprasus, Jacynth and Amethyst – there is no doubt that a permanent mark was left on a tender and romantic imagination. These are among the most familiar names of gemstones to the average person, although in fact many of them must have been different from the ones we know.

Hickorite, from Mexico, named for its resemblance to hickory wood, is not a fossil but the rock rhyolite, the 'grain' coming from flow patterns while still molten. It takes a good polish.

Right is a specimen of 'cockscomb' barite from Frizington, Cumberland. *Above* With a geologist's hammer for scale, is a vein of platy, crystalline barite, just as the miners would have found it underground. This was photographed many years ago at Bigrigg mine, also in Cumberland, where the famous hematite ('kidney ore') mining is still carried on, although the best specimens are no longer available. This area has several 'classics' which can be see in museums around the world. These include fine barite crystals (page 32), superb calcite crystals of all kinds (page 86), reniform hematite (pages 76, 79), as well as good quartz, dolomite and aragonite crystals.

This roadstone quarry at Meldon, Devonshire, England, is popular with collectors for certain metamorphic minerals, particularly wollastonite (see page 98), garnet, idocrase and axinite.

Of the high priest's gems, diamond referred to rock crystal, sapphire to lapis lazuli, beryl to peridot, while 'ligure' has not been positively identified. Jacynth is an old name for hyacinth (zircon). It is fairly certain the 'jasper' meant carnelian, particularly where the light from the New Jerusalem is described as being 'like unto a stone most precious, even like a jasper stone, clear as crystal'. Even carnelian tends to be cloudy, so citrine might be a more accurate translation.

While these are mostly familiar words which conjure up a gem with a certain colour, they are the exceptions in the mineral world. Most mineral names are not only unfamiliar but downright discouraging. Quartz, mica, gypsum, sulphur and graphite are common minerals recognisable to us as having everyday uses. But what on earth is one to make of orthoclase, plagioclase or oligoclase? They are in fact all individual sub-species from a group of similar minerals, collectively lumped under the title of feldspar. Feldspar considered as one mineral is even more common than quartz, and these old names are among the first one encounters in the study of mineralogy. As with many other sciences mineralogy draws heavily on classical languages for the nomenclature. In these three examples '-clase' refers to different habits of cleavage – from the Greek word *klasis* meaning fracture. Microcline, another feld-spar, also gets its name from its cleavage, although in this case it translates as 'small angle'. Other names of feldspars however vary widely in their significance. Labradorite was first noticed in Labrador about 1770; Albite gets its name from its white colour; 'moon stone' comes from the pearly lustre of another feldspar variety, while 'Amazonstone' gets its name from the green of the Amazon River, where it was first reported.

Even when you are familiar with some of the root words the particular application may be obscure. Pyrite and pyrope for instance have nothing in common but their similar name. The 'pyr' part (from the Greek *pyros*, meaning fire) describes different properties. Pyrite, a brass-coloured iron sulphide, gives off sparks when struck with steel. Pyrope (a silicate of the garnet family) is so named because of its fiery red colour.

You might be excused if you thought that arsenopyrite and löllingite were quite different minerals. They are in fact so similar they are almost impossible to tell apart without a laboratory test. The one is basically pyrite with an atom of arsenic replacing an atom of sulphur in the molecule. The other, named after the Lölling district where it was discovered, has arsenic replacing both atoms of sulphur (pyrite = FeS_2, arsenopyrite = $FeAsS$, löllingite = $FeAs_2$).

'Pyr' crops up again in pyromorphite, a green lead

chlorophosphate, which changes shape when strongly heated, and pyrolusite, a black manganese oxide, which has the property when heated with glass of 'washing' (in Greek, *lysis*) out impurities. Another black manganese oxide is psilomelane (*psilos* = bald, *melas* = black) because it often takes the form of rounded shiny black lumps. So it soon becomes apparent that there is no short cut. But one mustn't labour the difficulties with names too much, one has the same thing in everyday life. Take Mrs Francis Xavier Esquieros and Miss Molly Malone, identical twins.

Fortunately, one usually encounters fresh names in small doses, and by the time one has got used to the more common ones, most of which are pronounceable, one is ready to try rolling one's tongue around such names as posnjakite. This is a rare and newly-discovered mineral and anyone finding a specimen, however minute, would probably be quite happy to master its pronunciation.

It will be noticed by now that most endings are the same, with '-ite' or variations such as '-ine', and, more rarely, '-ote', '-ose'. However remote from the original they may be, they all appear to stem from the Greek word *lithos*, a stone. The habit of naming minerals for their physical attributes goes back to ancient times and it is only within the last two centuries that the use of proper names came into practice – presumably because of the difficulty of fitting the greatly increased number of known species and varieties with valid, concise descriptions.

Altogether there are some 2000 species of mineral recorded, and countless more varieties and sub-species. New ones are being discovered constantly, as techniques for identification improve. Specimens once dismissed as being imperfect examples of known minerals, often turn out on re-examination to be quite new and significant species. But this is the field of the specialist. The novice collector will have quite enough to keep him busy and happy with the two or three hundred established minerals which he stands a fair chance of running into, depending on what part of the world he lives. For those who wish to specialise in showy cabinet specimens, there are even fewer to be concerned with, at least to start with; and speaking of specialization, one can spend years devoted to one species and its varieties alone.

One of the first problems is to learn to be able to link the name of a mineral with a mental picture of what the mineral itself is liable to look like. The illustrations in this book have been chosen, therefore, not only for their obvious eye-appeal, but to include specimens showing how they are more likely to be encountered in the field. Also, as a means of learning to associate names with certain appearances or physical groups, the pictures have been arranged as far as possible (without sacrificing pictorial appeal) in 'collections' of various types.

Gold panning in Australia is still profitable for some. This is gold dust which has been brought in by aboriginal prospectors, for sale at the nearest store, in Halls Creek, Western Australia.

One's particular interest in minerals will depend partly on inclination and partly on circumstance. Circumstances include time to spare, cash available, where you are located, whether you are active and mobile, or limited by health. Inclination is of course a personal matter and may be dictated by a scientific bent or whether you are more influenced by the romantic or æsthetic appeal of the subject. Those living within an easy drive of agate fields (California for instance) or quartz gemstone beaches (the east coast of England and Scotland) will soon find themselves looking in rockshop catalogues for the price of tumblers and trimsaws. If you live in a city, with limited spare time, you may confine most of your interest to reading and tracking down collections in museums, and, if you have a bit of cash to spare, some judicious buying from dealers is a satisfying outlet for your interest.

Areas with mines or quarries will encourage specialization in one class of mineral or another. On the other hand, if your inclination starts to get control of you, you may find yourself setting off into the wild blue yonder with pan and pick, geiger-counter and UV light, dynamite and claimstakes strapped to the back of your burro (or Safari wagon, if you are rich).

So whether it is your destiny to spend weekends rooting out old mine sites; or to get the mad light in your eye which carries you off to arctic wastes or tropical jungles, mountain tops, or salt pan deserts; or simply to spend quiet hours at ease listening to madrigals on your ultraphonic stereo and basking in the glow of tourmaline from Brazil, azurite from Tsumeb, sulphur crystals from Sicily, opal from Lightning Ridge, brought to you through the ingenuity of hardy adventurers and acquired by the stroke of a pen, you will have to start somewhere and it could well be in the following pages.

Three crystal groups of sphalerite, the major ore of zinc. The top two are recent finds from the classic 'Tri-State' mining area of central USA. The lower one is from an old collection of English Cumberland minerals.

What is a mineral?

Chemistry is so closely linked with mineralogy that to touch on this subject is unavoidable. One can, in fact, define a mineral very simply as a chemical of fixed composition formed by natural processes. Many chemicals familiar in everyday life, and those on the chemist's shelves, are indeed taken from nature and used (after some refinement) almost exactly as found – sulphur and table salt for instance. Borax, epsom salt (epsomite), copper sulphate (chalcanthite), and saltpetre (nitre) also occur naturally as minerals.

One of the first chemistry experiments performed at school, demonstrating a simple chemical reaction, is the one in which iron filings are heated with powdered sulphur, so forming a sulphide of iron. A similar substance to this chemical, crudely and imperfectly made in our test tubes, is abundantly created by nature as the handsome, brass coloured mineral, pyrite, popularly known as 'fools' gold'. The experiment is then carried further by adding hydrochloric acid to the iron sulphide, producing that delight of small boys, sulphuretted hydrogen – a gas smelling of rotten eggs.

Of course there are many chemicals and minerals which do not lend themselves to such classroom entertainment, and are not to be found on chemists' shelves. You would not, for instance, go to a pharmacist for a packet of granular silicon dioxide. If you did need this chemical it would probably be for mixing with cement or filling up a sandbox. Because silicon dioxide (quartz), one of the commonest of all solid minerals, is, when powdered, better known as sand.

Many minerals such as those mentioned can be used unaltered as nature created them, while others are treated by heating and reaction with other minerals to form chemicals which do not, as a rule, occur naturally. A simple example is calcite or calcium carbonate (from limestone), which is heated in kilns to form quicklime, or calcium oxide.

Metal is probably the first thing that comes to mind when speaking of minerals, because metals play such an important role in our lives. The discovery of how to make the alloy bronze took mankind a massive step forward along the route to our present day concept of civilised living. The advent of iron gave its users a clear advantage over those still limited to softer metals. Nowadays, the variety of metals and their alloys which are essential to life as we know it seems to be endless. But they all started their existence in the earth as ores, usually in combination with other elements, particularly sulphur (sulphides) or oxygen (oxides), although silver and copper not infrequently occur as the pure metal, and of course the usual occurrence of gold is as itself, or mixed with minor amounts of silver.

Although it is natural to think of all minerals as being solid, by most definitions of the word, our old friend H_2O (water) is probably the commonest mineral of all (and its solid form, ice, is also plentiful). By a very free interpretation, 'mineral' also includes air, but since air is a mixture of *gaseous* minerals the atmosphere is by definition nearer to being a rock, a concept likely to make the mind boggle.

But however one thinks of minerals, practically every solid substance essential to man's well being, apart from some products of plant fibre and animal tissue, is originally extracted from the ground. This does not include food since the mineral content of our diet is, apart from salt and some vitamins, mostly obtained through the agency of vegetables. These do the job of breaking down essential minerals (calcium, iron, nitrates, phosphatates etc.) for the animals and ourselves who feed on them.

The contents of today's medicine cabinets are likely to include more minerals than those of the larder. Where once the apothecary may have found it profitable to stock such items as eye of newt, toe of frog, wool of bat – and indeed we still depend to a large extent on organic medicines such as microbe-corpses (vaccines) and the juice of mould (penicillin) – our mineral-based medication is a lot more sophisticated than the days when amethyst was used to ward off intoxication, bloodstone to cure nose bleeds and nephrite jade was considered the best antidote for kidney trouble.

But we come into contact with minerals in our every-day lives far more frequently than we may be aware of. When you pencil a note to the milkman you are using the mineral graphite (the 'lead' of the pencil) to make marks on another mineral which has been impregnated in plant fibres (paper). This other mineral may be gypsum, baryte, or china clay, depending on the type of paper.

Graphite appears in other guises besides that of the lead for pencils. It is used in the manufacture of paint, as a lubricant, in making electrodes, stove polish and so on. Baryte and gypsum are also used in the manufacture of paint. Gypsum is particularly important industrially, and is the essential ingredient of Plaster of Paris (so named for the extensive gypsum beds under and near that city). It is also used in the manufacture of crayons and rubber, as a fertilizer, and as a retarder in cement, to mention a few more.

The quest for metal

To begin at the beginning, the first tools used by the first creatures who could be called our ancestors were probably a mixture of animal, vegetable and mineral – sticks and stones, rocks and bones. But stone must have established itself from the start as the most effective and durable all-round material.

This is not 'fool's gold', but the real thing—a priceless specimen of crystalline gold on iron-stained quartz, from Rhodesia. Of all the precious minerals known to man, few are likely to turn his head more quickly than the mention of gold. In 1849, the great gold rush to California affected the course of history by speeding up the development of the western part of America. Even the rumour of gold is enough to stop a man in his tracks, and many a sailor has jumped ship, or a farmer abandoned his homestead, to join in a fruitless stampede after the yellow stuff. South Africa, Western Australia, Alaska, all have their histories of gold fever. But although so elusive in workable quantities, it is distributed in small parcels in every part of the world. It is interesting to compare this specimen with the delicate 'arborescent' crystals on page 54, which were embedded in limestone, that has since been partly dissolved in acid, leaving the insoluble gold standing free.

And certain types of stone, notably flint, were found to be better than others. Since good-quality flint is unevenly distributed over the surface of the earth, this meant that areas where the best flint was to be found attracted settlers and formed the basis for a more advanced culture and for trade. The first mining in man's history was for flint where it occurs in strata in chalk (for example, Grimes Graves in Suffolk, England). These burrowings are to be found around the world, but particularly in Europe, where prehistoric man has been so extensively studied. What is interesting is the complexity and high degree of engineering skill involved in these flint mines, and it gives an insight into the importance of obtaining the highest quality material for maintaining an increasingly improved standard of tool-making.

While searching for the flints, primitive man would inevitably find that certain rocks and stones were more attractive to look at than others. By their colour or markings, and the way they glowed or sparkled in the sunlight, they would be set aside as being worthy of possession for their own sakes. Perhaps the concept of beauty for beauty's sake was beyond the very primitive mind, and perhaps the feelings aroused by contemplating a pebble of amber, or a crystal of quartz, would have to be given a mystic significance–from which would be born the connection between gemstones and magic. But we do know that minerals in the form of roughly formed gemstones have been worn as ornaments and charms from the beginnings of human cultures.

The copper age, soon to be followed by the better-known bronze age, when metal first took over from stone as the prime material for tools and weapons, began a mere six thousand years ago. Considering that it had taken man a million years or so to progress from the crude chips of the palæolithic age to the polished implements of the neolithic age, this is a very recent event. But from this time on the history of mining becomes more and more involved. The first metals used by man to any extent were gold and copper, both of which are found in their natural state and could be worked without any elaborate processing. Bronze (an alloy of copper and tin) was a refinement which quickly followed the discovery of copper as a useful material for making tools and, more significantly, weapons.

Lead is another metal with a long history. The ease with which it can be extracted from its ores made it a natural discovery for the early metallurgists. Zinc on the other hand, a close associate of lead in nature, was slow to reveal itself, owing to the difficulty of separating it from sphalerite, its most important ore.

The Hittites are believed to have been the first to make use of iron in the strategic sense. A numerically unimportant race, they nevertheless left an impact on history by the military pressure they were able to exert by the use of forged iron weapons, which could make impressive dents in the bronze of their foes.

Next to aluminium, iron is the most abundant metal on the earth's surface. It has many ores, from rich lodes of hematite to very low grade 'ironstone' which is found in such massive quantities that it is nevertheless quarried in vast open mines in various parts of the world. Aluminium is another matter. Although present in most rocks (and many of the rock-forming minerals, notably the feldspars, are in effect silicates of aluminium), it is economically impractical to extract it from these. Corundum, the parent mineral for the precious stones ruby and sapphire, is a simple oxide of aluminium. This is a compound so hard that in nature only diamond is harder, and so stable that its metal does not part

Opposite page *Grime's Graves, a neolithic flint mine in Suffolk, England. Excavating was done with antler picks. Larger and finer quality flint nodules were to be found buried in the chalk than those found loose in gravel and on beaches.*

Above *A flint nodule from Sussex chalk.*

An outstanding group of sulphur crystals from Sicily. The amber colour is rare, bright yellow being typical. The bluish tinges on the right are reflected light. not the colour of the crystals themselves.

Proustite (ruby silver) from Charnacillo, Chile.
A superb specimen, but unless it is kept away from
the light, the colour will change.

easily with its oxygen component. But the major ore of aluminium turns out to be a crumbly, earthy, nondescript stuff called bauxite, which is also an oxide of aluminium. Such are the paradoxes of mineralogy – consider the extremes of natural carbon: diamond and graphite, the hardest and the softest of all. Other metals such as cobalt, chromium, nickel, manganese, titanium and tungsten play roles of varying importance in our lives, and are mostly late comers on the mining scene.

Apart from miners and those in the ore-extracting industries who utilise the products of mining, there are many people whose lives become intimately involved with minerals. First of all there is that rather outdated character, the prospector. He is the one who devotes his life to finding the locations where mining may be worth attempting. He may, if he has a good strike, change his role for that of a miner. But a dyed-in-the-wool prospector is more likely to get restless with one find and move on to fresh fields. Then there is the student of mineralogy who may rarely stray from his library or laboratory, and spends his time analysing, cataloguing, and perhaps writing learned papers on esoteric subjects. Research chemists may find their work spilling over into mineralogy, and many practical mineralogists and metallurgists working for industry are in fact research chemists. The hobbyist who makes no bones about his intentions, which are simply to enjoy all the other activities without assuming any of their responsibilities, is in a happy position. But these are only stereotypes, because there is a little bit of each in all of them. And they are all interdependent. The science of mineralogy needs people to find the minerals, people to extract them from the earth, others to study and analyse them, to catalogue them and finally people to enjoy the results of all this endeavour.

Classification

As with many sciences, mineralogy has only recently emerged from the dark ages. Although sound observations were being made even in Greek and Roman times, an astonishing legacy of superstition from the past was handed on uncritically. Possibly the first study to be considered in terms of the modern science was by Georgius Agricola (Georg Bauer). Born in Saxony in 1494, he was the author of a classic work *De re metallica*, published in 1556. In this he put forward some views on the formation of mineral lodes which were somewhat heretical for his time and pointed the way to a more scientific approach to the classification and study of ores and other minerals. He was perhaps the first to make a clear distinction between rocks ('heterogeneous minerals' as he called them) and minerals ('homogeneous minerals'). The 'homogeneous' minerals he subdivided into earths, salts, gemstones and other minerals. His book is illustrated with woodcuts giving us a wonderful pictorial record of mining at that time.

Above *This rugged individualist at Altunga, Central Australia, is one of the last of the gold prospectors. He is standing beside a contraption called a dry blower, part of his equipment for separating the elusive grains of gold from the masses of sand and gravel.* **Opposite page** *This remarkable woodcut from Agricola's* De re Metallica *gives a clear picture of what mining was like and the techniques used in the 16th century. It is not hard to see the connection between the gnomish figures in this picture and the mountain dwarfs of folklore. Note the one with a divining rod looking for more metal.*

Chalcopyrite crystals from St Agnes, Cornwall, showing characteristic irridescent tarnishing.

Cuprite (variant Chalcotrichite) from Fowey Consuls, Cornwall. A fine example of this rare, feathery formation.

Ein nützlich Berg
büchlin von allen Metal-
len/als Golt/Silber/Zcyn/Kupfer
ertz/Eisen stein/Bleyertz/vnd
vom Queckfilber.

Some aspects of mining, early and recent. **Opposite page** *Another engraving from Agricola shows an underground apparatus for raising water, a forerunner of the steam pump on page 36.* **Right** *The title-page of a book published at Erfurt in 1527. The German title means "A Useful Mining Manual for all metals, like gold, silver, tin, copper ore, iron-stone, and quicksilver".* **Above** *The vast dumps of this gold mine at Kalgoolie, Western Australia, contrast with the simple operations of the lone prospector* **below** *(see also page 22).*

28

Illustrations taken from two classics, James Sowerby's *British Mineralogy* (1811) and Philip Rashleigh's *Specimens of British Minerals* (1797), the former a monumental work in several volumes. Both are profusely illustrated with coloured engravings which may seem a little quaint to our eyes, but show a good understanding of the principles of mineralogy, which seems to have reached comparative maturity ahead of other natural sciences. It is interesting that mineral books written in the late eighteenth and early nineteenth centuries contain complex observations which could have come straight from a modern text book, and yet Charles Darwin's *Origin of Species* was still half a century in the future. Significantly, it was the period when chemistry was beginning to come into its own.

James D. Dana's *System of Mineralogy* was a milestone. His first works (from 1837) had followed an older system, but in 1854 he put the science of mineralogy on a firm footing which has remained basically the same until the present day.

Three plates from Philip Rashleigh's Specimens of British Minerals. *A fourth will be found on page 138. Rashleigh made an outstanding collection of minerals from the mines of Cornwall and Devon, the cream of which is now resting in the Truro Museum, Cornwall, and includes some of the finest examples of the rare and colourful minerals of that area. The drawing on the right shows black cassiterite (tin oxide) crystals in mica from St. Agnes, Cornwall. The other two, which are remarkable for their plant-like forms, both come from Matlock in Derbyshire, England. On the left is a handsome specimen of 'flos ferri', a stalactitic formation of aragonite (a carbonate of calcium). A more common crystal formation of this mineral is seen on page 33.* **Below** *An example of 'feathered' gypsum, called 'snow fossil' by miners.*

A fine crystal of blue barite on a mass of dolomite crystals from Mowbray Mine, Cumberland, England.

Another example of the range of colour found in fluorite, Illinois, USA.

32

Three of the illustrations on this page come from James Sowerby's British Mineralogy. ***Right*** *Lead ore from Derbyshire, showing bands of dark galena sandwiched between light-coloured layers of barite.* ***Below*** *A fossil ammonite sliced in half to show in-filling of crystalline calcite.* ***Bottom right*** *Slender crystals of aragonite from near Glasgow, Scotland.* ***Bottom left*** *This specimen of native antimony from Allemont, Dauphiné, France, is from Sowerby's* Exotic Minerals *(1811–17).*

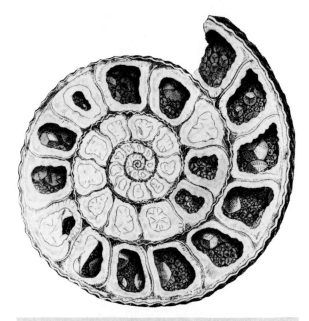

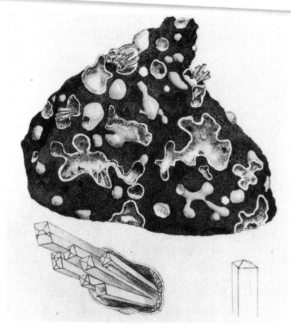

More plates from Sowerby's books. **Above** *Small cavities in basalt containing the zeolite mesolite.*

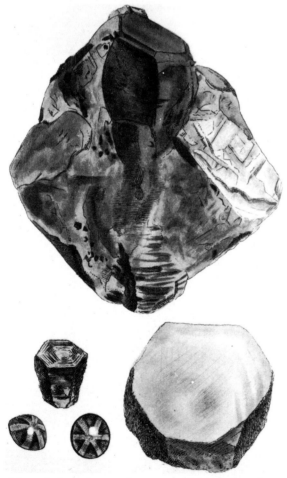

Rough apatite crystals in matrix.

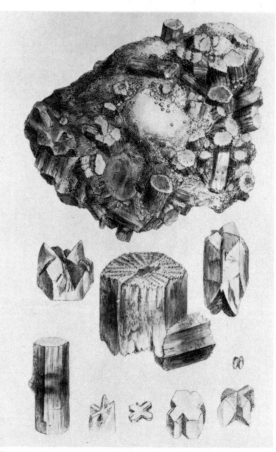

A barrel-shaped corundum crystal in matrix and two star-sapphire cabochons. Apatite and corundum crystallize in the hexagonal system.

These aragonite crystals show pseudo-hexagonal form due to 'twinning'.

Many means for classifying minerals had been in use, often variations on Agricola's simple grouping. Although chemistry was usually the basis, this was not as straight forward as it might have been and could include such rather vague terms as 'alkaline, earthy', 'acidiferous alkaline', 'metalliferous', and 'combustibles'. There were many who advocated a grouping on the lines of the genera used in botany, but assigning genders to minerals belonged to the age of alchemy and the times demanded something less fanciful. The system called 'economic' divided minerals under the headings of 'metallic' and 'non-metallic', which were subdivided into rather arbitrary classes based on both chemistry and physics. These were divided again into groups, dictated by the dominant element. But this proved unwieldy.

Dana (pronounced Dayner) based his system simply on chemistry. Improved methods of chemical analysis made this not only possible but the most logical approach; and it is still the basic form of classification used by mineralogists everywhere.

The study of minerals can easily become an end in itself. Many mineralogists devote their lives to isolating and classifying species regardless of whether the minerals themselves have any relevance outside an index or as other than crystallochemical oddities. This is the true scientist at work, and the end product is scientific fact. But the original impetus has always been the practical demands of society.

The need for known minerals, whether they be flints or uranium ores, is bound to stimulate study. It is imperative to find out where to look for more when the present stocks run out, and the study of minerals has always been linked with mines and mining, in other words the study of minerals of economic importance–whether metallic ores, gemstones, or clays.

In eastern Pennsylvania, not far from Bethlehem, there is a small wood where the ground has been much disturbed at some time. Here one can find very attractive specimens of red and yellow jasper, as well as carnelian, chalcedony and quartz. Once it was the centre of an Indian trade in these materials which were used for making arrow heads and ornaments. Jasper from Vera Cruz (the name of the nearby village) has been found far from its place of origin, which suggests that it must have been highly prized by the stone-age American Indians. This is one example of primitive mining operations.

The first organised efforts to win minerals from the earth were the flint mines already mentioned. These were, in some places, deep and complex workings consisting of shafts and tunnels. But since these were in soft chalk, the primitive antler picks

Leadhills, once a rich mining district in southern Scotland, still yields small quantities of gold from some streams.

were adequate for the job. Ores of metal are normally to be found in veins embedded in rock that is considerably harder than chalk. So the first ores to be used by man were certain to have been found loose as boulders or pebbles.

The beds of certain streams would be a profitable source of some metals. It is well known that river beds in areas of gold-bearing rock are likely to yield gold dust and perhaps the odd nugget, and this is where gold was first found and worked. Tin is another metal which has been taken from river beds since early times, in the form of dark, heavy pebbles of **cassiterite**, the oxide of tin. The Phœnicians are known to have sailed to islands in the northern waters that they called the 'Cassiterides' to trade for the local tin. These are presumed to be the Scilly Isles, off the tip of Cornwall, or even Cornwall itself. The streams of that corner of Britain have certainly been a major source of tin since prehistoric times.

Once the resources of the stream showed signs of being used up, the next step would be to excavate the rock where the minerals showed on the surface. The first mines of this kind were simply shallow pot holes and trenches. Traces of these exist in mining areas all over the world, where man reached the stage of working metal. Miners of more recent times have been well aware of these ancient workings and usually refer to their remote predecessors as 'the old men'.

The next development would be the sinking of shafts to follow the veins down into the heart of the rock. The illustrations from Agricola give some idea of the extent to which this had progressed by the Middle Ages. But here an obstacle was encountered which sooner or later limited the depths at which these mines could operate. This obstacle was water. The water table varies according to the rock structure, height above sea-level and other factors, but, when reached, nothing but efficient pumping will permit any deeper operations. The first use to which steam power was put was in fact that of operating the pumps which kept the deep mines open. The first successful steam engine was produced in 1712 by Thomas Newcomen, an English blacksmith, twenty-four years before the birth of James Watt, who is generally believed to have invented the steam engine from scratch by watching a kettle boil. Watt's true contribution was to make outstanding improvements on known principles, as was Trevithick's after him. The tall brick and stone buildings built to house the rather ungainly high-pressure engines soon became a part of mining scenery everywhere, and their ruins are still in evidence, particularly in Cornwall. Quite a few of the engines were working continuously for over a century, until the day their services were no longer required. The last, at Robinson's Shaft, South Crofty, stopped work in 1955.

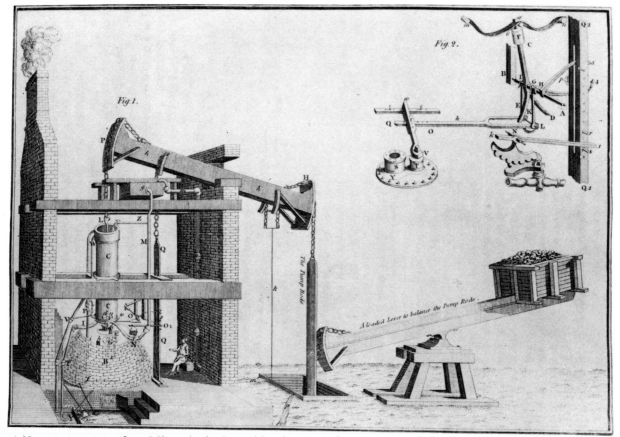

A Newcomen engine from Mineralogia Cornubiensis *(Cornubia = Cornwall) by William Pryce, 1778. Note the counter-balancing beam.*

The sight of one of these derelict engine houses may well quicken the pulse of a rockhound, for this is often the first sign he has that 'game' is at hand. Hillocks, often overgrown, are usually to be found nearby, consisting of waste from the old workings, and they may well contain minerals which were overlooked at the time or discarded as being useless for the miners purposes.

Disused quarries are rarely productive for the collector. Quarries are usually worked for building materials, solid rock preferably without mineralization. Any loose rock is likely to have been removed at the end of operations. Working quarries, on the other hand, are sometimes among the best hunting grounds, if permission can be obtained, and this will be gone into on page 119.

Right *A typical 19th-century whim (winding engine) restored by the Cornish Engine Preservation Society, along with the nearby pumping engine on page 38. Many of these engines ran virtually non-stop for over a hundred years, well into this century. The last one was re-erected in 1927.* **Below** *Ruins of Levant mine near Land's End. This has recently been re-opened.*

*Pumping engine at East Pool, Cornwall with a
90-inch diameter cylinder.*

Looking at minerals

When Agricola made the first clear distinction between rocks and minerals by describing the former as 'heterogeneous' and the latter as 'homogeneous', he put his finger on the essence of the matter. A rock –granite for instance–can vary in composition quite considerably before it becomes a different rock. Granite properly consists of quartz and orthoclase feldspar in major proportions, with lesser amounts of mica, tourmaline and/or garnet etc. But there is never any exact rule for the proportions, nor could there be, since the composition of a rock depends on chance–the chance assemblage of material at the time of its formation. Otherwise, every slightly different rock would need a new name.

If, however, a mineral should vary in composition in the slightest degree, it becomes a different mineral. Even if the arrangement of atoms in the molecular structure changes, you have a new mineral.

Any reader to whom chemistry is a bit of a bore is at liberty to skip the next page or two, but those who stay will find that some basic chemical knowledge is essential for a complete understanding of the subject. If you already know your chemistry, bear with us.

To start with ABC. The smallest particle of matter as we understand it is an atom. The composition of atoms is not our concern here; we all know what happens if they are split. Of all substances known to man there are more than ninety which cannot be reduced to a simpler form: these are the elements. Reduce an element to its smallest possible part and you have an atom, something so small as to need the kind of analogies that are used to describe the vastness of the universe. One such analogy goes like this: suppose the earth were entirely made up of soil on which nothing grew except grass; suppose, again, that one wanted to calculate the number of atoms in a speck of matter the size of a grain of sand; the answer to the latter is in the former–the number of atoms would be about the same as the number of blades of grass on this global lawn.

So much for the atom, but what of the molecule? The old-fashioned concept of the molecule as a simple entity, consisting of minimum numbers of atoms arranged in a set pattern, is no longer tenable. When dealing with chemical formulæ, it is tempting to think of them in this way, because this is what is implied. But the 'molecule' of a chemical formula is in fact an abstraction. One might simply call it the lowest common denominator of a chemical sub-

A section of porphyry from Scotland, showing crystals of feldspar embedded in finer-grained rock.

39

stance. It is a convenient analogy to compare atoms with people, tending to pair off or gang up to form molecules. But it is inaccurate and misleading.

When describing the composition of a given chemical substance, such as quartz, it is hardly practical to say that it consists of so many silicon atoms with twice the number of oxygen atoms, closely interwoven in a geometrically constant lattice! To a chemist or a mineralogist it is enough to give the symbol SiO_2. And if the reaction of two chemical substances could be described (to take an elementary example) as the union of x atoms of oxygen with $2x$ atoms of hydrogen producing x 'molecules' of water, how much easier it is to say that $H_2 + O = H_2O$!

Of the ninety-odd natural elements, all have one or two-letter symbols. Usually it is based on the initial letter of the element. Where two elements have the same initial, the first one on the table of elements has the single letter, and the others are qualified by a second letter (hydrogen = H, helium = He). In a few cases, the symbols are based on the Latin names: for example, Au = Aurum (gold), Ag = Argentum (silver), Sn = Stannum (tin).

The symbol for a mineral (or chemical compound) indicates the number of atoms in its molecules. Thus the mineral **smithsonite** (zinc carbonate) is shown as $ZnCO_3$ or one atom each of zinc and carbon to three of oxygen. The equation for the creation of smithsonite is as follows: H_2CO_3 (carbonic acid) $+ Zn = ZnCO_3 + H_2$. In other words, if you add the correct amount of zinc to a given amount of carbonic acid, they will rearrange their atoms, with hydrogen being released and a residue of zinc carbonate (smithsonite) left. (When you see the plus sign in a chemical equation, it serves to separate two or more elements or compounds.)

This has considerable bearing on how minerals are formed in natural conditions. Carbon dioxide (CO_2) is a small but persistent part of our atmosphere, and in ancient geological times it was a significant part. When the atmosphere becomes saturated with water vapour, the carbon dioxide will combine with it, forming carbonic acid ($CO_2 + H_2O = H_2CO_3$). Of course, it is highly diluted in more water, but in geological time this is of minor importance. The carbonic acid which acts, however slowly, on the minerals with which it comes into contact, creates new minerals out of old. Zinc carbonate can be created through the slow erosion of zinc sulphide by this relentless exposure to carbonic acid, however weak.

The first scientific method used in the identification of minerals was the chemical one, and this is still in wide use. More advanced techniques depend on equipment which is beyond the means of most individuals, but a simple home lab is easy to acquire and use. Serious prospectors will even take portable labs along for use in the field, if they are likely to be away for any length of time.

While still on the subject of chemistry, the chemical formula for a mineral is the key to its mineral class. A single initial denotes an element, for example, S = the element sulphur. S at the end of the formula (FeS_2) indicates a *sulphide*. The ending SO_4 indicates a *sulphate*, derived from sulphuric acid, and so on.

Salts, oxides and silicates

A large number of minerals belong to the general class of *salts*. These are essentially the result of metals being dissolved in acid, and the hydrogen of the acid being replaced by the metal – as in the case, described above, of zinc in carbonic acid. Another example would be $HCl + NaOH = NaCl + H_2O$. In words, caustic soda in hydrochloric acid becomes rock salt (halite) and water.

Complete lists of chemical classifications of minerals can be looked up in the text books listed in the bibliography at the end, but two groups should be mentioned before moving on. These are the *oxides* and the *silicates*, neither of which qualify as true salts, but which provide a number of important species. Quartz, in fact, can be classified under either heading, being an oxide of silicon. The ending for oxides is usually O_2. Hydroxides contain an extra atom of hydrogen, while hydrous oxides have molecules of H_2O tagging along with the oxide molecules.

Silicates may be quite simple, or diabolically complex. **Rhodonite**, a pink silicate of manganese, is $MnSiO_3$. The formula for the gem **tourmaline** once moved John Ruskin to observe that it was more like the concoction of a mediæval alchemist than the ingredients of a respectable mineral. The formula being one or another variation of:

$$Na(Al,Fe,Li,Mg)_3B_3Al_3(Al_3Si_6O_{27})(O,OH,F)_4$$

Examples of some of the salts of the commoner acids:

Hydrogen sulphide (H_2S)	sulphide	PbS (galena)
Hydrochloric acid (HCl)	chloride	NaCl (rock salt)
Hydrofluoric acid (HF)	fluoride	CaF_2 (fluorite)
Carbonic acid (H_2CO_3)	carbonate	$CaCO_3$ (calcite)
Nitric acid (HNO_3)	nitrate	KNO_3 (nitre)
Sulphuric acid (H_2SO_4)	sulphate	$CaSO_4$ (anhydrite)
Phosphoric acid (H_3PO_4)	phosphate	$Fe_3(PO_4)_2 \, 8H_2O$ (vivianite)

Rock

It might be as well to consider some of the related material which the collector will run into sooner or later. The first of these is, of course, rock. The difference between *rock* and *mineral* should be clear by now. Rock is, roughly speaking, all the stuff of which the earth's crust is made. There are many kinds of rock which can be defined, within limits, but none of them can be pinned down with the exactness which is expected of a mineral.

In fact the word 'rock' can have different meanings in different places. Americans, for instance, will speak of 'a rock' meaning the same thing that in England would be called 'a stone'. That is, a piece of rock (or stone) – larger than a pebble but smaller than a boulder – which can be picked up and thrown. In England, 'throwing rocks' would imply a battle of giants!

'Stone' is frowned on in scientific usage as being too loose a term, with too many imprecise meanings. The very term 'rockhound' is misleading because it is used to describe mineral collectors rather than geologists. Gemstones will be discussed under minerals since that is what most of them are, although, as already noted, there are some which have an animal origin (pearl and coral) or are derived from vegetables (jet and amber). Other precious and semi-precious stones, being a mixture of minerals, are actually rock such as lapis lazuli and obsidian.

Meteorites are of course in a class by themselves since they originate from space. Looking for meteorites is something of a specialised business, with luck playing a large part. They are usually rather unprepossessing to look at and could easily be passed over. In fact, the likeliest way to find them is to be in some area where a shower has recently been recorded. Meteorites are generally one of three kinds, metallic, stony or a mixture of the two. The metal is chiefly nickel-rich iron. Indeed, iron rarely occurs in its native state on earth except in meteors.

Other stones, which it is assumed also originate in outer space, are called *tektites*. These are glassy like obsidian and when found may be in odd tear-shaped droplets. They are something of a mystery, one of the more appealing theories being that they are fragments of lunar rock thrown into space by the impact of giant meteorites, although nothing so far from the Apollo reports has backed this up.

Fulgurites, on the other hand, are of strictly terrestrial origin. These are odd-looking objects, hollow, and twisted like gnarled roots or dried branches, and are formed when sand is fused by lightning.

Fossils are very much the study of the geologists, but quite often fossils have been altered to or replaced by certain minerals, and these make attractive additions to a mineral collection. Calcite is frequently found in the fossils of limestone, while other minerals which may be associated with fossilisation are pyrite, opal, agate and flint. One of the most attractive are agatised sponges to be found in Tampa Bay, Florida.

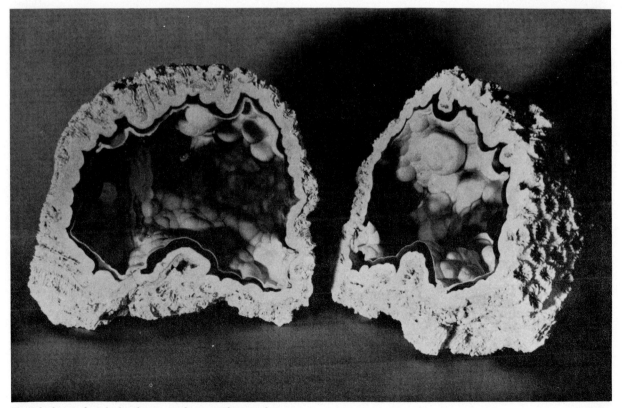

Two halves of a chalcedony geode, pseudomorphous after coral, showing fine botryoidal formations inside, from Tampa Bay, Florida.

Concretions are interesting in that they are the result of a similar process to that which deposits minerals in cave formations, in fossils and the creation of certain geodes. They may come in many shapes and sizes – sometimes regular, and almost artificial-looking, sometimes lumpy and nondescript. They may be largely made up of clay cemented by a mineral such as calcite, or they may be all mineral, as in the case of the flints and pyrite nodules abundant in parts of chalk beds. Of particular interest are clayey concretions which have cracked on hardening to form a network of fissures in its interior which then fill up with some mineral, usually calcite, but occasionally barite, pyrite, gypsum or certain others. This cracking may be revealed on the outside as a maze of lines or ridges, or it may not show until the nodule is sawn or broken open. These are known as 'septarian nodules'.

*Various concretions are shown here. **Left and opposite page, bottom** Clayey, spherical nodules of the type known as 'cannonballs', from County Durham, England. **Opposite page, top** A section through a brown septarian nodule, revealing the cracks filled with yellow crystalline calcite. Polished, these make attractive ornamental specimens. **Below** A fragment of a septarian nodule from the Isle of Sheppey, Kent, England. This has a coating of yellowish calcite, criss-crossed by a grid of tiny pyrite crystals. Other nodules from the same location contain 'sprays' and 'rosettes' of barite crystals (see the large specimen on page 102). Concretions are characteristic of sedimentary rocks.*

Perhaps a word about *Moon rock* would not come amiss at this point. Long before man landed on the moon, mineralogists and others had speculated, often wildly, on the possibility of strange and splendid mineral specimens which they hoped would be found there. The possibility of a new range of minerals unknown on earth, or of a glittering treasure of giant crystals, of gold and precious stones, lingered on in the imagination. But now, with the hauls of the most spectacular rockhunts of all time in the bag, the picture which has emerged so far is of a much more limited range of minerals than we have on earth. The lack of an atmosphere and consequent weathering is largely responsible for this, since a high proportion of our minerals are the result of chemical changes brought about by the action of air and water.

One surprise is the high proportion (over 10% in the Apollo 11 samples) of **ilmenite** (an iron-titanium oxide) in moon rock; another is the rarity of quartz (less than 1%), but this may well be a local phenomenon. The fact of quartz being the most abundant mineral of earth rocks has already been mentioned. The moon's minerals, far from being grandiose crystal specimens, have all been on a microscopic scale. One or two new ones have been identified, but these are close in composition to species already known on earth.

The rocks so far examined have mostly been of types similar to basalt and dolerite, which accounts for the lack of quartz and the predominance of plagioclase, pyroxene and olivine–all minerals typical of the dark igneous rocks of earth. So perhaps, with millions of square miles still to be explored, there may be good crystals of peridot (gem olivine) waiting to be found, and who knows what else.

Identification

One of the first questions asked about any mineral is how one knows what it is. The answer is not always easy, nor is it always as precise as the answer a gardener may give when asked about the identity of a plant. The gardener can point to all kinds of detail, the sort which can easily be illustrated in a manual. Unless confronted with a typical specimen from a known locality, the mineralogist may have to rely on a combination of several inconclusive factors such as weight, colour, lustre, cleavage, hardness and 'streak', all of which will be explained below. Association with other minerals (if any) can be an important clue. But in many cases a conclusive identification is not possible without laboratory testing. One must often be content for the time with a vague 'one of the grey copper ores' or 'probably an amphibole or a pyroxene'. The clincher is usually in the crystal form, if this is visible. Again, some minerals are so distinctive that a couple of factors may be enough.

To start with colour, it must be said straight off that this, unfortunately, is perhaps the least reliable of all means of identification. Although some shades of colour are associated almost exclusively with one mineral (the carmine pink of **erythrite**, the pistachio green of **epidote**), the colours of others may run the gamut of the rainbow and beyond. Fluorite, quartz, tourmaline and beryl are but a few of the more obvious. I, for one, would like a penny for every time that purple fluorite has been mistaken for amethyst. Here a penknife will quickly provide the correct answer: if the point of the blade can make a scratch on the material, it is fluorite (perhaps the variety known as 'Blue John'), if not it is almost certainly amethyst. If quartz scratches it but the penknife will not, it has to be purple glass.

Which brings us to the very important identification factor of *hardness*. Most minerals keep very close to a given position on a recognised scale of hardness. The most widely used is the one devised by Professor Fredrich Mohs in the early 1800s. The scale starts at *1* (talc, the softest) and ends at *10* (diamond, the hardest), with eight other minerals distributed as evenly as possible in between, each higher one on the scale being able to scratch the one below it, and being in turn scratchable by the one above.

Scale	Mineral	Common object for testing
1	talc	fingernail
2	gypsum	
3	calcite	cupro-nickel coin
4	fluorite	
5	apatite	penknife or glass
6	feldspar	steel file
7	quartz	
8	topaz	
9	corundum	
10	diamond	

Specific gravity (relative weight) is another fairly constant guide. This is not so easy to estimate without proper equipment, but quite often, when one is exploring a mine dump for example, one notices that the odd piece may be heavier or lighter than its neighbours. This is not only a cue for a closer investigation, it may be a vital clue to its name.

One of the more elusive, but important, characteristics of a mineral is its *lustre*, or the way it reflects light. At one extreme there is 'adamantine' lustre, the most brilliant of all, of which diamond is a perfect example. At the other extreme you have 'earthy' or completely devoid of lustre. There is no even gradation between one and the other, as in hardness. There are many diversions in between, partly induced by the degree of opacity or transparency. A high lustre on an opaque substance is described as 'metallic'. 'Sub-metallic' is one degree less than this. 'High lustre' is usually associated with transparency; but some quite clear minerals may have a relatively poor lustre, connected with a low refractive index–the angle at which a substance *bends* light.

Other types of lustre are self-descriptive. 'Vitreous' (or glassy) is a degree less brilliant than 'adamantine'. 'Porcellanous', 'resinous', 'pearly', 'silky' and 'waxy' speak for themselves.

Another vital clue to a mineral's identity is found in the way it breaks. An ordinary break is called a *fracture* and may be 'even' (flattish), 'uneven' (rough), 'hackly' (gritty), 'earthy' or 'conchoidal' (shell-shaped, like the curves of a clam). A more significant way of breaking is called *cleavage*. This is closely related to its crystalline structure, and a plane of cleavage often has the clean sharpness of a perfect crystal face. Many minerals have no cleavage, which can also be a factor in identification, others may cleave in one, two or more planes. Cleavage may be rated as 'poor', 'fair', 'good' or 'perfect'. Orthoclase feldspar has two good cleavages and one fair. The micas all have one perfect cleavage (as good an example as you can get of what cleavage means). Galena and halite have a cubic cleavage (three planes). Fluorite, under the right conditions will cleave into a perfect octahedron (four cleavage planes), while sphalerite has a dodecahedral (twelve-sided) cleavage in six cleavage planes.

*Top Conchoidal fracture in obsidian. Flint and glass share the same type of fracture. **Right** The cubic cleavage of galena. **Below** Fragments of a piece of calcite, showing how this mineral splits up into rhombohedral cleavages.*

A test which, when it is positive, can often be conclusive is the *streak* test. A number of minerals, if ground up to a powder, show a distinctly different colour to the original. One good example is **pyrite**: the powder of this brassy-yellow mineral is black. The powder of shiny black crystals of **hematite** is brick-red. The quick way to find this out is to scratch the material across a 'streak plate', that is to say a piece of hard, unglazed tile. (I have found that a ceramic pestle or mortar is ideal.) The colour of the streak left behind is the answer.

Light-coloured minerals are unlikely to leave a mark. Many dark ones, particularly silicates, likewise leave no distinct mark. But a good example of the value of a streak test can be found when confronted with certain specimens which are uniformly black and knobbly ('botryoidal', as described on page 00). There are four fairly common minerals which under certain conditions are found in this form. Two are oxides of iron, **hematite** and **goethite**; the other two are oxides of manganese, **pyrolusite** and **psilomelane**. The streak test will produce one of three possible results: if the streak is black, the specimen is either one of the manganese oxides; but it might also be yellow-brown, or red, and the answer to the former is goethite and to the latter, hematite.

Another black oxide of iron, called **magnetite**, is, as its name suggests, strongly *magnetic*. Very close to magnetite, and once considered to be the same mineral, is maghemite, which has the property of being able to attract particles of iron to itself, and is better known as 'lodestone'. Lodestone was the basis for the earliest compasses. **Pyrrhotine**, or 'magnetic iron pyrite' is another example. A certain variety of hematite in soft shiny black flakes (micaceous) is also sometimes magnetic.

Lodestone from Arkansas. The 'whiskers' of iron filings demonstrate its magnetism.

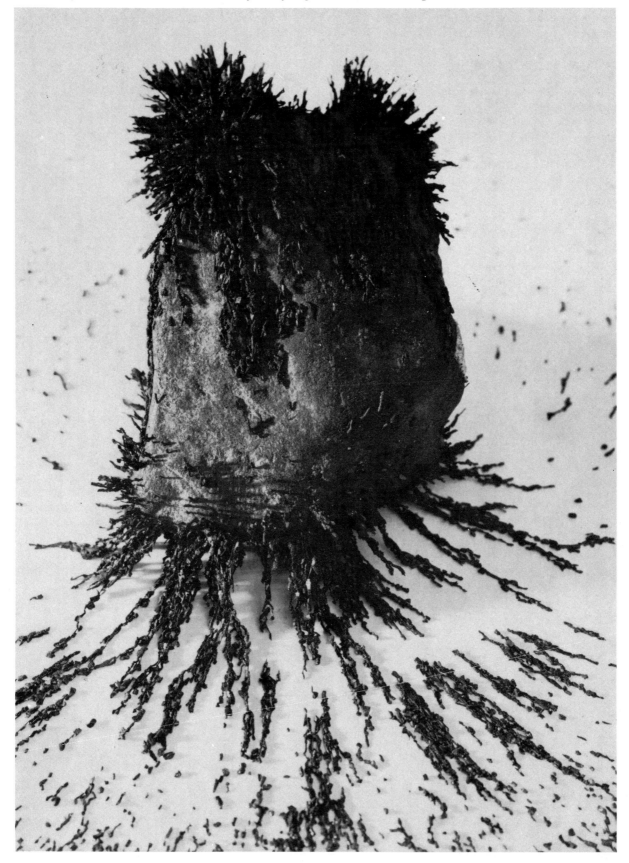

Certain minerals are interesting because of the optical characteristics they possess, in other words, the tricks they play with light. For instance, a very clear variety of calcite known as **Iceland spar** (because it was discovered in Iceland) will, when placed on a picture or printed page, give a double image of what is there.

Ulexite, a sodium calcium Borate, is sometimes found in compact fibres like satin spar. If this is sliced across the fibres to give two flat ends (which should be polished), and placed on print or other marks on paper, as with Iceland spar the image in this case will be transmitted along the fibres directly from one end of the ulexite section to the other, giving

it an effect which has earned this mineral the name of 'T/V spar'.

A third mineral, this time a fluorite of sodium and aluminium called **cryolite**, has a special claim to fame apart from its odd optical property, because it is almost a one-site mineral. Quite abundant in Arksukfiord, West Greenland, where it is mined for use in the manufacture of certain types of glass and the production of aluminium, it is almost non-existant elsewhere. The peculiarity is that it reflects light at almost exactly the same angle as water, and powdered cryolite immersed in water becomes nearly invisible.

These specimens have two things in common. Firstly, they are both associated with countries in Arctic regions. Secondly, they have optical properties which make them unique. **Above** *Iceland Spar demonstrates its characteristic of double refraction. (It should also be noted that it demonstrates an almost perfect rhombohedral cleavage).* **Right** *Dark rhombohedral crystals of the iron carbonate siderite in a matrix of cryolite.*

Above *Yellow orpiment, from Utah and orange-red realgar, from Nevada, are popular with collectors, although realgar has a disconcerting way of converting to orpiment if exposed to too much light. Both are sulphides of arsenic. Another mineral whose colour, a rich velvety green, makes it a natural choice is malachite.* **Right** *Usually associated with knobbly, botryoidal specimens or polished slabs showing a wavy banded structure, malachite may also occur as small fibrous crystals, as shown in this example from Wales.*

Radial structure in wavellite from slate quarries.

The interior of a pyrite nodule from the chalk.

The real key to visual identification is in *form* — crystal form above all. This doesn't mean that one can dispense with other factors if one has a perfect crystal. Even crystal form duplicates itself in very different minerals. A splendid example of this is the specimen from Cave-in-Rock, Illinois. It has fine cubic crystals of two quite different minerals, **fluorite** and **galena**. The one is a deep, transparent purple, while the other is the typical silver-grey of lead sulphide. They are both identified by a combination of crystal form (the same) and colour-lustre (quite different). An extra aid to identification is the association: fluorite and galena are very frequent companions.

Crystals are not the only distinctive form assumed by minerals. There is a number of indeterminate forms typical of certain minerals which can be aids to identification. Most familiar are the knobbly, bumpy, rounded surfaces which are known by the descriptive names of 'botryoidal' (shaped like a bunch of grapes), 'reniform' (kidney-shaped), and 'mammillated' (bosomy!). When the knobs run together in a columnar structure it is described as 'stalactitic'. Sometimes, these rounded forms, when split, can be seen to be caused by radiating, crystalline fibres; in some cases these are needle-like crystals whose terminations represent the outside of the bump (as with wavellite or hematite).

Above Wollastonite *(see page 98)*.

50

Four different types of formation. **Opposite page, bottom left** Reniform structure in hematite. **Top** Filiform (wiry) structure shown in a specimen of native silver from the classic location at Kongsberg, Norway. **Below** An example of botryoidal form taken from smithsonite (zinc carbonate). **Right** Stalactitic limonite, or brown oxide of iron.

Opposite page *A remarkable specimen of the manganese carbonate rhodocrocite (from the Greek rhodon = rose) from Sweet Home mine, Colorado, USA. Rhombohedral crystals of this quality are the most valued. More familiar is the stalactitic variety with its pink wavy bands, often cut and polished into ornamental or gem stones.*

Below *Another pink manganese mineral, the silicate rhodonite. This crystal group comes from the classic location at Franklin, New Jersey, USA (where over 140 species have been reported). It includes two other typical Franklin minerals, black franklinite (zinc-rich magnetite) and green willemite (a silicate of zinc).*

Other non-crystal forms may be wiry (silver, copper), 'tuberose' or root-shaped (flos ferri), 'arborescent' or like branches of a tree (copper) or 'dendritic', filmy, fernlike patterns (pyrolusite). Others may be hair-thin prismatic crystals, 'fibrous', 'capillary', 'acicular' or 'columnar'—or infinitely thin layers, 'scaly', 'micaceous', 'lamellar' or 'foliated'. 'Bladed' and 'platy' refer to crystals that are more than usually flattened.

Mineral formations continued. **Opposite page, top** *A vein of fibrous chrysotite (asbestos serpentine) in serpentine rock, illustrating fibrous structure.* **Bottom** *Two examples of inclusions in crystal quartz—golden 'needles' of rutile (rutilated quartz, left) and black needles of tourmaline (right).*

Dendrites are fern-shaped deposits on rock, usually of the black manganese oxide, pyrolusite **(opposite page, centre right)** *They are not fossil plants, but form rather like frost on window panes.* **Opposite page, centre left** *A beautiful specimen of arborescent (tree-like) gold crystals, from Hopes Nose, Devonshire, England. The arborescent formation is illustrated* **below** *by a fine specimen of native copper from the classic location in Michigan.*

Below One of the richest colours in the mineral kingdom is the deep viridian green of the silicate of copper, dioptase. So rare are good specimens that even tiny ones fetch a high price, and this one from Tsumeb (in South-West Africa) measures several inches across.

Opposite page Of the crystals sometimes found in pegmatite rock (see page 110), apatite is one of the most attractive. A mineral of many colours, these lilac hexagonal prisms from Saxony are particularly fine. Apatite is also a widely distributed rock-forming mineral.

Crystals

As for the crystals, these are based on six three-dimensional geometric forms known as **1** isometric or cubic **2** hexagonal **3** tetragonal **4** orthorhombic **5** monoclinic **6** triclinic. Before groaning about more technicalities to digest, let us take a look at them and try relating them to familiar objects.

Firstly *isometric* ('equal measurements'), also known as *cubic*, is like a cube of sugar or a child's building block.

Hexagonal is the shape of most lead pencils.

Tetragonal, a square prism (two equal dimensions and one different), can be represented by the box that roll film comes in.

Orthorhombic is a rectangular form of which a match box is a good example – each dimension being different.

Monoclinic is similar but with one pair of opposite sides sloping. The nearest example that comes to mind is that kind of eraser which has sloping ends.

Triclinic is difficult to match with an everyday example. One must imagine a monoclinic (one sloping side) shape in which each pair of opposites have somehow slipped forming angles greater (or less) than 90° to their neighbours.

These figures are only meant to indicate the *frame-*

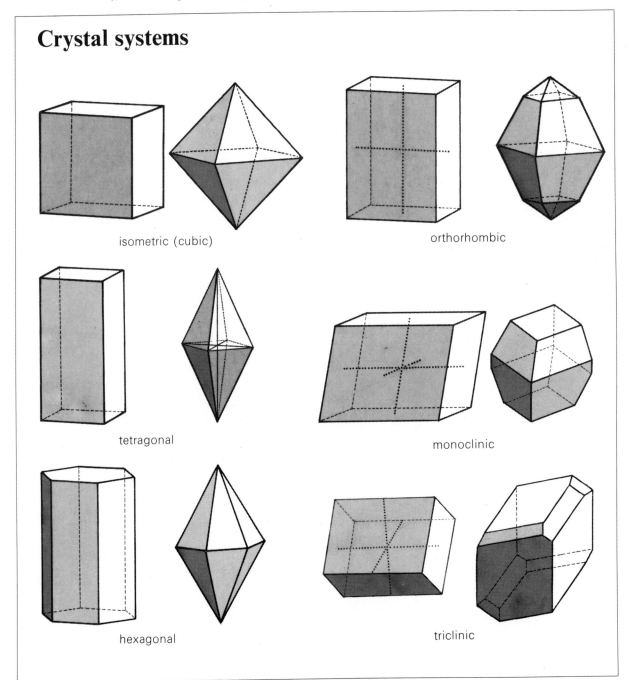

Crystal systems

isometric (cubic)

orthorhombic

tetragonal

monoclinic

hexagonal

triclinic

work of a crystal, a framework into which the crystal will fit neatly. The figures indicate the outside limits. For example, although an isometric crystal may fit exactly into the cube form, it could have its corners cut off, or carried further it could be an octahedron with only its points touching the cube. The variations on this theme are almost unlimited, but always the framework is the same. And this applies to all the other crystal systems. Where the measurements are unequal, as in a prism, an unequal dimension may be longer or shorter than the others. Taking the example of the pencil, the unequal axis (length) is usually longer than the axes of the cross section, but a hexagonal crystal can be stumpy, shorter than its cross section. So it can be seen that within these simple frameworks there is an enormous variety of possible crystal shapes.

Another factor to consider here is the tendency for some crystals to double up on themselves, to grow together at odd angles, often producing a quite different *apparent* crystal shape. This phenomenon is called 'twinning'. Fortunately for the sanity of mineralogists, a given twin formation is normally characteristic of a specific mineral. But it can be confusing all the same.

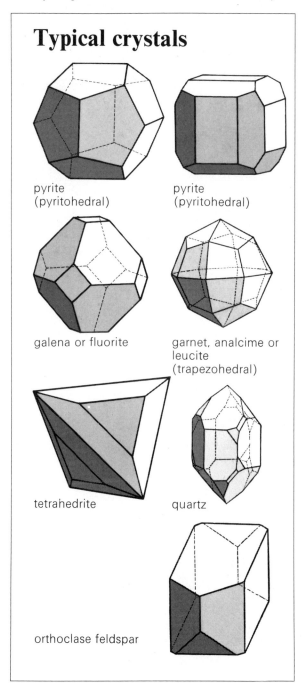

Typical crystals

pyrite (pyritohedral)

pyrite (pyritohedral)

galena or fluorite

garnet, analcime or leucite (trapezohedral)

tetrahedrite

quartz

orthoclase feldspar

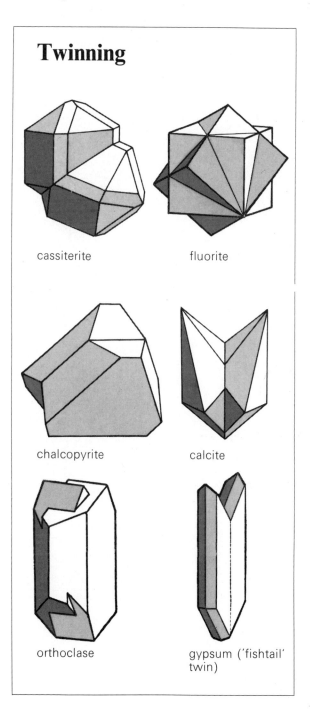

Twinning

cassiterite

fluorite

chalcopyrite

calcite

orthoclase

gypsum ('fishtail' twin)

59

A hexagonal prism of aquamarine from a cavity in granite in the Mountains of Mourne, Ireland, with crystals of feldspar and smoky quartz.

Fine crystals of orange-red hessonite and pale green diopside (a pyroxene), from the Italian Alps. The numbers were marked for the study of crystal angles and faces.

Fine crystals of orange-red hessonite and pale green diopside (a pyroxene), from the Italian Alps. The numbers were marked for the study of crystal angles and faces.

What can be even more confusing is the fact that one mineral can change to another, retaining its original crystal shape. This is called a *pseudomorph* ('false shape') and it may happen in a number of ways. Pyrite can change to the brown oxide of iron (goethite) if its sulphur atoms are replaced by those of oxygen (plus some H_2O). This process is similar to the rusting of iron. The molecular structure changes, but the outside shape of the original crystals remains the same.

Another, simpler type of 'false shape' known as *epimorph*, is the result of a thin crust of one mineral completely enveloping the crystals of a second, superficially assuming their form. Another kind of epimorph occurs when one set of crystals is enveloped by another mineral, the first dissolving or decomposing and leaving a mould—the impression of its shape—within the second mineral. Then a third mineral is deposited inside this mould, and if the second is somehow removed, a cast of the first is left. This complicated and unlikely-seeming process happens more often than might be supposed.

Yet another variety of pseudo-morphism which should be mentioned is the *paramorph*, where there is no change in composition. For example, aragonite changing to calcite (both $CaCO_3$) or wurtzite to sphalerite (both ZnS). This often happens when a mineral is only stable at a high temperature, and changes to another structure on cooling.

*Various types of pseudomorphism. **Below** A small piece of slate containing a cubic crystal of pyrite. The larger piece of slate has square cavities (or casts) from which pyrite cubes have weathered out, (both specimens from Ballachuilish, Argyllshire). **Opposite page** Casts of triangular crystals (chalcopyrite) in shale. **Right** An interesting specimen: originally, two large twinned crystals of feldspar formed in the granite of the Cornish china clay district; the surrounding rock weathered away and the feldspar partly altered to china clay. These loose crystals of altered feldspar are not uncommon in the district, where they are known as 'pig's eggs'.*

Chrysoprase (a chalcedony) from Queensland,
Australia, a source of some of the best specimens.
It is apple-green all through, and its other colours
in this picture are due to the action of the lighting.

Various formations of pyrite crystals. **Right** *Small intergrown cubes from clay-limestone cliffs near Lyme Regis, Dorset, England.* **Below** *A fine group of cubic crystals from Elba.* **Bottom** *Five small specimens including an octahedral crystal resting on a large cube (centre) and three interpenetrating cubes (right).*

Opposite page *Chrysopraze (a chalcedony) from Queensland, Australia, a source of some of the best specimens. It is apple-green all through, and its other colours in this picture are due to the action of the lighting.*

By this time you may be wondering how crystals occur in the first place. Indeed, it is a common reaction, when first confronted with the mysterious perfection of natural crystals, to imagine they must be the work of an eccentric gem cutter, or to have been created by some mechanical means. In fact, crystals can no more be created than flowers. Those crystals that are said to be grown in laboratories are simply the product of a natural process, like hot-house plants, even if the conditions are artificial.

To speak of crystals 'growing' is natural, since they can increase in size while maintaining their general shape, but it must be remembered that this is a different process from biological growth. In the latter case, the growth takes place from the inside, working outwards. Crystals grow from the outside by accumulation, and to do so it is obvious that there must be more of the same material around to make the addition to the original.

This can be demonstrated in your own kitchen by dissolving copper sulphate, or some other water-soluble salt (table salt will do, but is not so effective) in hot water until the solution can hold no more; and the hotter the water, the stronger the solution can be. Conversely, as the water cools, the copper sulphate is 'squeezed' out of the solution. When this

happens the precipitate starts to gather around any nucleus, preferably of its own kind, that it can find. If, for instance, a small piece of copper sulphate is suspended by a thread in the solution, it will be an ideal nucleus, and will start to grow as a crystal. Growing crystals of various water-soluble salts can be an interesting pastime in itself.

So, for the creation of crystals, at least two conditions are needed: the material for their construction and elbow-room to grow in. The solutions that offer the best conditions for this are not necessarily hot water. They may be liquid, molten rock, superheated steam or various others allowing free movement of the constituent atoms. Since crystals need time to grow, it follows that the largest will be the result of the slowest possible cooling of the solution. In the case of rock, it is a fact that when molten lava is ejected from a volcano, the resulting rock is very fine grained, due to rapid cooling. Molten rock which cools deep under the surface does so very slowly, resulting in coarse-grained rock, such as granite, in which the separate minerals can easily be picked out without any magnification. If there are pockets (air or steam 'bubbles') in this rock, they are often lined with crystals of fair size, because they were allowed the elbow-room to grow in.

Below *A geode in basalt lined with quartz crystals and fluorite (from Gourock, Renfrewshire, Scotland).*

Bottom *Unusual wedge-shaped crystals of barite (from Settlingstones, Northumberland, England).*

A walk through the mineral gallery of a museum will quickly confirm what must be obvious by now, that minerals come in all shapes and sizes and every imaginable colour and shade, from dull to brilliant. The most beautiful ones are invariably those with large, lustrous crystals, but some may need a microscope to reveal their quality. Some may look like fine glass or porcelain, others like chunks of coloured resin. Many will have the appearance of polished metal while others simply look like dried mud or caked rust. Some, it will be obvious, occur in large quantities, while others rarely turn up in more than thin crusts or films on other minerals. The chemical grouping of minerals is not much help in indicating what to expect. One can say that the *sulphides* tend to look like metals, but there are several sharp exceptions to this rule. One can say that the *silicates* never show a metallic lustre, but they do cover about every other lustre you can think of. Silicates tend to be above average in hardness, but talc and soapstone are silicates, as well as several other soft minerals.

Because of this, I have found it convenient to arrange minerals into a series of broad groups, based partly on their appearance, partly on their uses and partly on their mode of occurrence. This is by no means a substitute for the proper chemical arrangement, but is simply a sort of rule of thumb for getting to know how and where the minerals occur, and what they are. The headings used for these groups are as follows—*spars, ore minerals, rare and micro* (usually occurring in very small crystals), *rock-forming minerals* and *gemstones*.

It must be emphasised that this is arbitrary and not at all scientific. For one thing, many minerals come under more than one of these headings, and different observers might pick different headings as the first choice for a given mineral. Most mineralogists would put **garnet** under the heading of metamorphic rock-formers, although this can also be found in igneous rocks (some granites for instance). The average reader would probably class it as a gemstone, which of course it often is as well.

Spars

The word spar is an old one used by miners and others to describe certain common light-coloured minerals. A spar is usually white or colourless, cream, greyish or in other pale tints. It often shows good cleavage faces, and, with one exception among the common spars, is not unduly heavy. The exception is baryte (barytes) a sulphate of barium, known as heavy spar. Other minerals coming under this heading are fluorite (fluor spar), gypsum (satin spar), calcite (calc spar), dolomite (pearl spar) and, of course, feldspar. Cross-course spar was a name given by miners to the white, mineral-bearing quartz

of certain veins. In fact, spars often make up the bulk of 'gangue', that is to say the waste, non-ore material from mineral veins. Most carbonates are typical spars.

The collector is likely to encounter this group before any other because it is so widespread. He also stands a fair chance of finding crystal specimens of them. Good crystals of quartz, fluorite, calcite, and baryte are common in many areas.

Ore minerals

Ores as such are often a mixture of minerals, rich in the metal that is being mined, but here we are concerned with the individual minerals. Most ore minerals are either sulphides or oxides, with carbonates as close runners-up, although ores may come from any group. Silicates, in spite of being in the overwhelming majority of all minerals and containing large quantities of metals are very reluctant to part with them. Aluminium, for example, in combination constitutes 8% of the earth's crust. But separating it from any of the dozens of silicates in which it occurs is not economically feasible. There are exceptions, of course: rhodonite (manganese), hemimorphite and willemite (zinc), chamosite (iron), and dioptase (copper) are all silicates and potential ores.

A spread of spars. **Far left** *'Satin Spar', fibrous gypsum from Nottinghamshire.* **Left** *'Pearl Spar' or dolomite, from Cumberland—a good example of the small, slightly curved crystals habitually formed by this mineral.* **Above** *Inside a large geode of celestite from the classic location at Yate, near Bristol. Celestite is a sulphate of strontium whose crystals are not unlike those of barite (sulphate of barium), but is much less common.* **Right** *Witherite is a carbonate of barium, rather rare except for mines near Hexham, Northumberland.*

Ores are often coloured, or darker than the surrounding vein stone. Sulphides frequently have the appearance of metal: freshly broken galena (lead sulphide) has the brilliant lustre of molten lead, and it tarnishes to the same leaden grey of its parent metal. Unlike lead, it is very brittle and breaks up into distinct cleavage fragments. Pyrite, on the other hand, does not look like iron at all, but very much like brass, or even gold – hence the nick-name 'fools gold'. Chalcocite (now internationally renamed chalcosine), a sulphide of copper, looks more like lead, while niccolite (renamed nickeline), a sulphide of nickel, looks like pale copper. But most sulphides are silvery, leaden or iron grey. This goes even more for the sulpho-salts, a group with a rather more complex structure than the simple sulphides; tetrahedrite and bournonite are good examples, both containing antimony with sulphur as well as copper and other metals.

The most important copper ores are sulphides, of which there are several. Heading the list is **chalcopyrite** (chalco = copper), similar in appearance to pyrite but a deeper, more brassy yellow and having a tendency to acquire an iridescent tarnish. Tetragonal crystals are not uncommon. **Chalcosine** is a grey sulphide which crystallises only rarely. **Bornite** is a distinctive light bronze colour on freshly broken surfaces, but tarnishes rapidly to purple. This tarnish is sometimes so vivid as to earn the mineral the title of 'peacock ore'.

Another interesting sulphide is **molybdenite**, the chief ore of molybdenum. It is remarkably similar to graphite in appearance, that is to say it occurs as thin layers of soft, silvery grey material with a similar hexagonal crystal structure, but the lustre of molybdenite is usually brighter, with a bluish hue.

Stibnite is a sulphide of antimony with very distinctive prismatic crystals which may be leaden or steely grey. This is a 'must' for any general collection, and if you can acquire even one crystal from the classic site in Japan at Ichinokawa, you are really in business. These outclass any other stibnite crystals by a big margin.

Some assorted ores. **Opposite page** *Chalcopyrite (copper ore) crystals on white dolomite, from the Tri-State district, USA.* **Bottom left** *Crystals of galena (lead ore) from Cumberland.* **Below left** *Witherite crystals (strontium ore) from* *Northumberland.* **Below right** *Chalcosine (copper ore) from Cornwall—very rare in such large crystals.* **Bottom right** *Molybdenite (molybdenum ore) from Australia.*

Some notable exceptions to the generalisation that sulphides look metallic are sphalerite (zinc sulphide) cinnabar (mercury sulphide), proustite (silver arsenic sulphide), pyrargyrite (silver antimony sulphide), and the sulphides of arsenic, orpiment and realgar.

Sphalerite has a lustre sometimes described as resinous. Its colour may range from yellow to brown, through red to black. 'Black Jack', as the latter is known, has a sub-metallic lustre. **Cinnabar** (the ore of mercury) may occur as red crystals with a sub-metallic or adamantine lustre, but its more familiar form is a bright red with earthy lustre. This has been used as a pigment since palœlithic times. **Proustite** and **pyrargyrite** are both silver ores and, because of their colour, known as 'ruby silver'. Proustite in particular may be bright transparent red; pyrargyrite is a darker red and the lustre of both is adamantine. Since they blacken on exposure to light (the principle of photography), the best specimens in museums are kept in darkness and can only be seen on request.

Realgar and **orpiment** are brilliantly-coloured arsenic sulphides with a resinous lustre, the former orange-red, the latter a bright yellow. Both are used as pigments (orpiment is a corruption of the Latin *auri pigmentum* meaning golden paint), although today they are synthesised for this purpose. Realgar decomposes on exposure to light and air, and it too should be kept in a dark place.

A handsome group of sphalerite crystals (zinc ore) from the Tri-State district, USA.

Below *Needle-like crystals of millerite (nickel sulphide) in dolomite, from Wales.*

Bottom *Arsenopyrite crystals from Mexico (the source of arsenic).*

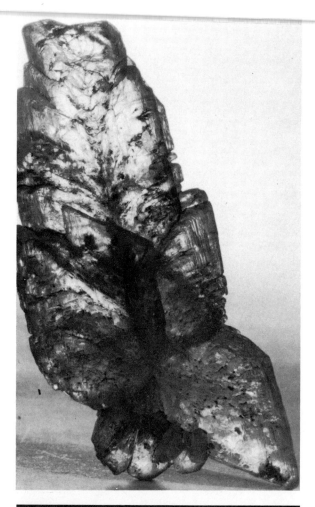

A geode of celestite from Gloucestershire

Above and top *Two interesting specimens of gypsum crystals (selenite), twinned in the form known as 'fish tail', from the London Clay.*

*Classics from the now defunct mine of Herodsfoot,
Cornwall, are* **left** *bournonite ('cogwheel' ore) and*
above *tetrahedrite with quartz.*

Oxides are less easily recognised as such. They cover every colour and lustre in the book. They include many very hard minerals; **corundum** (aluminium oxide) is second only to diamond in hardness but **bauxite**, a hydrous aluminium oxide is a crumbly material at the softest end of the scale. Some, like the hydrous iron oxide **goethite** or its earthy variety **limonite**, may vary in hardness from 1 to nearly 6 on the scale (limonite is, in fact, natural rust). Iron oxides are represented in several minerals. The most valuable ore being **hematite**. The word, from the Greek *haima*, meaning blood, refers to the basic redness of its colour. Although in pure crystalline form it is quite black, as noted before, it gives a red powder when crushed. It occurs in several interesting forms besides the usual bladed crystals. Best known are the reddish-black mammillary or reniform hematites from Cumberland, England, the 'iron roses' from the Swiss Alps, and crystals of specular hematite from Elba.

Earthy hematite is softish and a brick-red colour – not surprisingly, since red bricks are so coloured by the presence of iron oxide. It colours sandstones and certain clays and the pigment red ochre. (Yellow ochre comes from limonite.)

Another interesting iron oxide is **magnetite**. As its name suggests it is magnetic (a quality described on page 00). It is also black, and when crystallised takes the shape of octahedra. **Goethite** (named after the German poet) is a pure, crystalline limonite which may be botryoidal and black like some hematite but is easily distinguished by its yellow-brown streak.

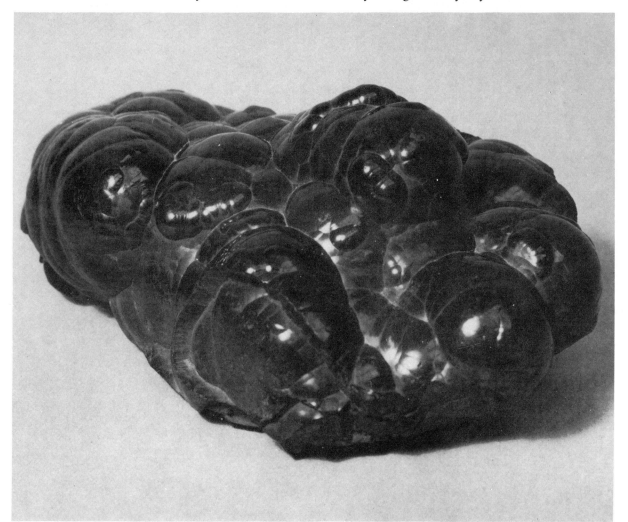

*Some iron oxides. The **above** classic example of Cumberland hematite was buried in the rockery of a London pub until I drew it to the landlord's attention! Well over a foot long, it is up to museum standard, but a sad example of how good specimens can go astray unless recognised as such.*

*__Right__ is another hematite classic, an 'iron rose' from Switzerland. **Top left** is a small reniform formation similar to the 'pub hematite', but of the brown iron oxide, goethite, from Bolallack, Cornwall. **Top right** Reniform goethite showing the internal radial structure.*

The chief ores of manganese are the black oxides **pyrolusite** and **psilomelane**. Distinctions between the two must be left to more technical works, but it should be noted that pyrolusite is the mineral which forms delicate fern-like patterns in the cracks of some rocks known as *dendrites*. **Manganite**, another black manganese oxide is distinctive for its steely lustre and prismatic crystals.

Cuprite is a red oxide of copper crystallising as octahedra, and in the variety known as **chalcotrichite** as fine, hair-like needles. **Cassiterite**, the main ore of tin, also an oxide, is hard with an adamantine lustre, usually brown to black but shades to yellow and cream at times. **Pitchblende**, named for its appearance, is an oxide of uranium and its chief ore.

Turning now to the ore carbonates, you will remember that this chemical group is typically representative of the spars. But some members, siderite (iron), cerussite (lead), rhodochrosite (manganese), smithsonite (zinc), malachite and azurite (copper), fit more comfortably under the heading of ores. What is most characteristic of all, and an important factor in identification, is that they all dissolve in an acid with effervescence. In some cases the acid must be hot and strong, in others it may be cold and relatively weak. Calcite, for example, responds readily to this test. A number of them share with calcite its characteristic rhombohedral cleavage (siderite, rhodochrosite and smithsonite). Of the ore carbonates, **siderite** comes in shades of brown, beige and often a coppery red-brown. **Smithsonite** is naturally whitish but may be coloured yellow, blue or pink because of trace impurities. Its typical occurrence is in botryoidal crusts. **Rhodochrosite** is rose pink, pale to deep and not to be confused with the manganese silicate rhodonite, which is harder. Rhombohedral crystals are characteristic although the massive form with rounded layers, similar to some malachite, is prized for decorative uses. Sharing with rhodochrosite the distinction of being the most colourful of the carbonates are those of copper.

More examples of oxides. **Left** *Pyrolusite pseudomorphs after manganite (both black manganese oxides) from Australia.* **Above** *A stalactitic psilomelane cluster (another black manganese oxide).* **Top left** *One large rough crystal of cassiterite (tin oxide) from Tanzania contrasted with tiny brilliant crystals of the same from Cornwall.* **Top right** *A piece of Cumberland hematite collected recently.*

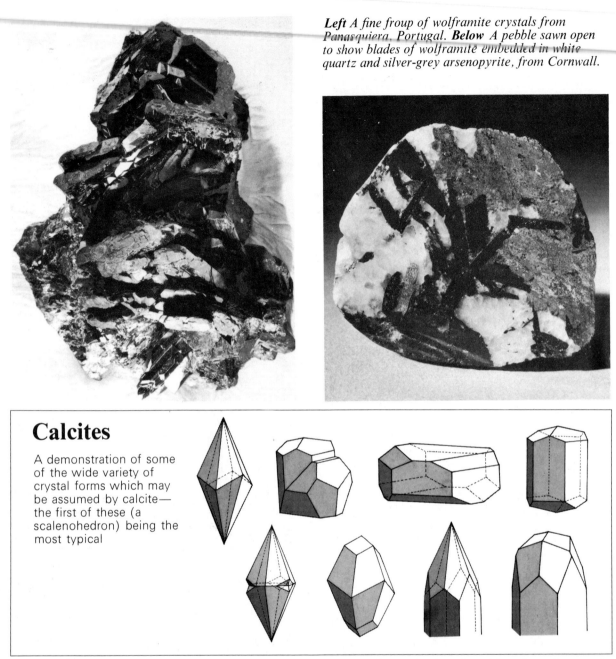

Left A fine froup of wolframite crystals from Panasquiera, Portugal. Below A pebble sawn open to show blades of wolframite embedded in white quartz and silver-grey arsenopyrite, from Cornwall.

Calcites

A demonstration of some of the wide variety of crystal forms which may be assumed by calcite—the first of these (a scalenohedron) being the most typical

Malachite, the best known, shades from emerald to a deep velvety green. The typical botryoidal formation, when sawn across, may reveal an opulent pattern of circular or wavy lines. **Azurite**, as its name implies, is a rich royal blue, good crystals being collectors' items. Malachite is its constant companion and they are frequently found on the same specimen.

A rarer but no less attractive carbonate also contains copper, as well as zinc. This is **aurichalcite**. The colour here is a pale turquoise blue, and when the fine, feathery crystals are found on a matrix of orange brown limonite one has one of the most superb natural colour combinations of the mineral world. **Rosasite** is very similar in all respects and distinguishing between the two is a job for experts.

Cerussite is likely to be yellowish, colourless, or snowy white. It is often found in prismatic crystals, scattered at random, like a bunch of white sticks. But again, the crystals may be organised into a geometric, triangular lattice. Next to galena, from which it is derived by the action of weathering, cerussite is the main ore of lead.

The primary ore minerals of tungsten are in a group of their own, the tungstates, and are very different to look at. **Wolfram** is dense black with a sub-metallic lustre, and a distinct cleavage plane (which is usually seen on rough specimens), typically as 'blades' embedded in white vein quartz or other material. Free-growing crystals are rare. **Scheelite** is light coloured, pale brown or green with a near adamantine or glassy lustre. It fluoresces strongly under short-wave ultra-violet light.

A superb group of quartz and green tourmaline crystals from a Brazilian pegmatite.

Rare and micro

From the major ore minerals (of which the foregoing was an incomplete sample) it is a short step to the lesser ores. These will be lumped together with others under the general heading of 'rare and micro'. This somewhat awkward and unorthodox title is a bit more specific than 'miscellaneous', and has been chosen with collectors in mind, since it includes many of their favourites.

Studying a major mineral collection arranged in the standard chemical order, one may notice that certain groups, which have not yet been mentioned, often have certain points in common. The phosphates, arsenates, vanadates, chromates (and to some extent the chlorides and sulphates) show a high proportion of brilliantly-coloured crystals, ranging in size from small to microscopic. The difficulty of making generalisations in the mineral kingdom is very apparent at this point. There are some obvious exceptions, and individual minerals may differ completely from the general trend.

For example, the phosphates include several comparatively rare colourful species usually found only as small crystals: torbernite, autunite, pyromorphite, vivianite and so on; but apatite belongs to the rockforming group, putting it out of the 'rare' class. The sulphates include a large number of copper minerals (and others) which fit the category, yet calcium sulphate (gypsum) and barium sulphate (baryte) are among the more obvious spars.

Persevering with this rare/colourful/micro category, because it is one of the more attractive ones for the collector and contains some of the really challenging species for the specialist, we will have to accept some loose generalisations. Most of this group are secondary minerals derived from primary ore minerals or from other secondaries. There are so many of them that it is difficult to know where to start, and impossible here to do more than make a few random comments.

Among the more interesting members of this group are pyromorphite (lead chlorophosphate), mimetite (lead chloroarsenate) and vanadate (lead chlorovanadate), classic examples of how a mineral of one chemical group can belong to a series which carries over into other groups. The typical colours of each are respectively green, yellow and orange-red. Each has the same crystal structure and forms, hexagonal prisms of various kinds with similar variations. The so-called 'barrel-shaped crystals' often found in pyromorphite are repeated in the brown-orange variety of mimetite—campylite, found only at Dry Gill in Cumberland. Vanadinite likewise shares peculiarities of crystal form with pyromorphite and mimetite, particularly the hollow prisms seen in the pyromorphite specimen illustrated on The copper minerals run riot in this category. Every variation and shade of green and blue are represented among their chlorides, sulphates, phosphates, arsenates and so on. Aurichalcite and rosasite, already

mentioned under carbonates, qualify for this group as well.

Some arsenates worth noting for their colour are pink erythrite (cobalt), apple-green annabergite (nickel), yellow-green adamite (zinc), blue-green scorodite (iron). Good specimens of these are much sought after, as are those of crocoite, a bright orange chromate of lead; and wulfenite, a molybdate of lead with distinctive thin tabular and platy crystals, green-yellow, brown or similar colours.

To appreciate this group a good magnifying glass is usually essential. Even better is a binocular microscope of $\times 30$ to $\times 40$ magnifying power. These are not necessarily as expensive as might be feared, and can be bought second-hand at quite reasonable prices, while there are also inexpensive Japanese models on the market which are adequate for the rockhound. Binocular microscopes are basic equipment for collectors of 'thumb nails' and micromounts—a micromount specimen being less than an inch in its maximum dimension (and usually mounted in a suitable box for protection), and 'thumb nails' are just one size larger, about $1\frac{1}{2}$ inches. The advantage of this type of collection is that some thousands of specimens can be stored in a space no larger than an average drawer.

Some crystal groups for collectors. **Above** *Lens-shaped crystals of brown siderite (iron carbonate).* **Opposite page, top** *Hemimorphite (zinc silicate) crystals from a current classic area, Sta. Eulalia, Mexico.* **Bottom** *A lattice of cerussite crystals (lead carbonate) from Tsumeb, South-West Africa.*

Crystals of pale, smoky quartz, and the rarely crystallized rose quartz, from Ita Bira, Brazil.

Orange, iron-stained quartz (Eisenkiesel') and black hematite (specularite) from Cleator mine, Cumberland, England.

Various calcite crystal forms. **Top left** *A small 'rose' from Cornwall.* **Top right** *A brown-coated group of 'dog tooth' crystals from Sta. Eulalia, Mexico.* **Above** *A group of large prisms from an old classic location, Egremont, Cumberland.*

Above *Smithsonite from south-west Africa.*
These pale blue-green rhombohedral crystals are
rare collector's items; smithsonite usually forms in
botryoidal crusts. ***Top*** *Small dogtooth calcite*
crystals lining a cavity in limestone, from Dorset.
Right *Dogtooth calcite from Cumberland.*

Opposite page Crystalline quartz specimens. From left to right: (back) amethyst, rutilated quartz; (centre) rose quartz, citrine; (front) hematite-coated amethyst, rock crystal, cairngorm.

Below Crystals of gems. The large specimen is ruby in green zoisite, with, left to right, 'watermelon' tourmaline, ruby two emeralds and beryl. *Bottom* Chalcedony varieties round a large agate. Clockwise from the top: chalcedony—carmelian tiger-eye, jasper-agate, an agate pebble, three agates and agatized rhyolite.

Well-formed 'books' of muscovite mica crystals from Brazil.

Large almandite garnet crystals in schist from Austria.

Rock-forming minerals

The most abundant of all minerals are the ones which go to make up the bulk of the earth's crust. This very large group of 'rock-forming' minerals is completely dominated by the family of silicates. There are others of course. Limestone is made up very largely of the carbonates calcite and/or dolomite. Apatite (a phosphate), magnetite (an oxide), and pyrite (a sulphide) also come under the heading of rock-formers, but in a minor rôle. So the time has come to take a closer look at the minerals containing the element silicon.

This is the hardest of all chemical groups to generalise about. Nearly every degree of the characteristics of minerals is represented—colour, lustre, hardness and so on. Various common tests on silicates tend to be negative, and the streak-test rarely shows colour. They resist the action of acids and heat. Positive identification often involves rather expensive laboratory equipment. On the other hand, many silicates are easy to recognise on sight, or at least the family group to which they belong.

Silicates tend to come in families. Mica, garnet, feldspar are not the names of individual species but of mineral series of which each member is closely related. The familiar silvery mica used in oil-stove windows is called muscovite. Dark brown to black mica is called biotite. Lepidolite (rich in lithium) is often a delicate lilac colour in aggregates of fine scales. Phlogopite, shades of brown, is often crystallised, and is the mica most frequently used in electrical appliances. These are just a few of the commoner micas.

Feldspars are harder to tell apart, because their colours tend to be similar pale shades, but their crystal shapes are often distinctive. In a few cases, colour can give the answer: only one feldspar is green, a variety of microcline known as 'amazonstone'. Plagioclase feldspars are a group within a group and include albite, so named for its white colour. Labradorite is a dark grey with a bluish iridescence when seen from certain angles, and sometimes qualifies as a gemstone. Some oligoclase has reddish-gold inclusions which have earned for it the name of 'sunstone'. Garnets all have the same crystal form, generally dodecahedrons (twelve faced) or trapezohedrons (twenty four trapezium shaped faces), but they range in colour from white, yellow, brown and red to black and brilliant green (uvarovite garnet, coloured by chromium). Pyrope garnet is a deep ruby red as mentioned earlier. Hessonite is also known as 'cinnamon stone' for its colour.

Detail of smaller 'books' of muscovite mica.(see opposite page).

Biotite mica crystals in cacite from Madagascar.

Albite feldspar crystals from pegmatite, from Brazil.

Small melanite garnet crystals, from California.

Fluorescence under long-wave ultra violet light.
Below Naturally blue-green fluorite from Heights mine, Durham, England, fluorescing purple.

Bottom Small lemon-yellow scales of autunite (phosphate of calcium and uranium) from Devon, fluorescing a bright yellow-green.

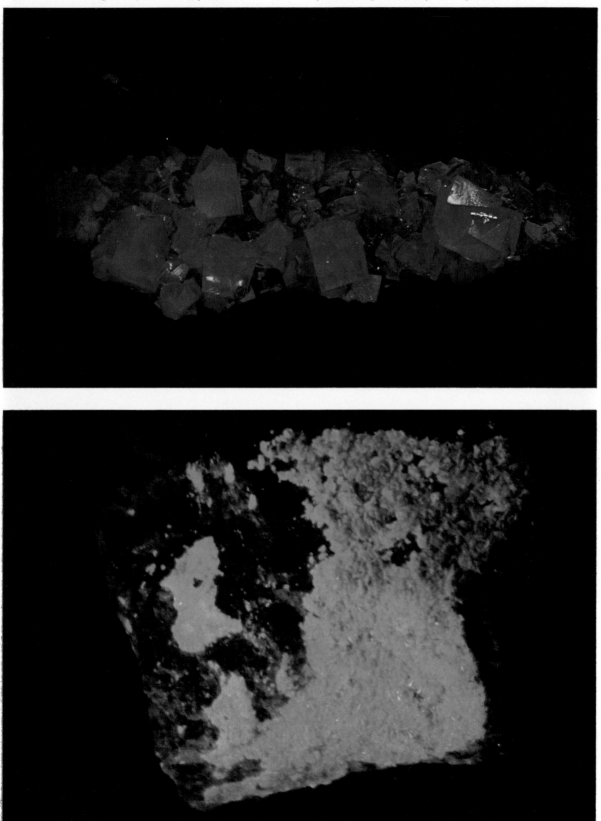

Some cabinet specimens, including chrysopraze, malachite and amethyst. 'Rare and micro' specimens are in front, with a small binocular microscope for enjoying their detail.

Other families include chlorites (green or brown mica-like, scaly minerals), amphiboles and pyroxenes (typical of dark igneous rocks, usually green to brown to black), and zeolites (a special group which will be described later).

If one thinks of rock as a sort of a porridge or a cake whose ingredients are minerals, one can get a fair idea of what one is dealing with. The ingredients tend to be similar, mixed up in different proportions. It is as if the master baker had bins of quartz and assorted feldspars, amphiboles and pyroxenes, large jars of olivine, serpentine, garnets, micas and chlorites; also a good stock of calcite and dolomite. For seasoning there are zeolites, tourmaline, topaz, apatite and so on. He has some favourite basic recipes which repeat themselves quite frequently, as well as variations on these, the occasional experiment, and a few special creations. As in any cuisine, there are a few elementary rules of mixing. Some ingredients just do not go with others. But this analogy should not be overdone, because it could lead to some misconceptions about the formation of rocks, and why certain minerals are more likely to be found in one kind of rock than another.

In the next chapter the basic rock types will be described in some detail but here it should be pointed out that there are essentially three classes of rock, *igneous* (molten rock that has cooled and set hard), *sedimentary* (laid down in deposits of mud, sand, chalk lime etc.), and *metamorphic* (igneous or sedimentary rock altered by heat or pressure or both).

Whitish stilbite (a zeolite) and glassy apophyllite are often found together. This specimen comes from a famous zeolite source near Poona, India.

94

Top left *Augite, a pyroxene, from Kenya.* ***Top right***
Chabazite, a zeolite, in basalt, from Skye, Scotland.
Above *Fine quartz crystals from Cornwall.*

A close-up of the torbernite crystals described at the end of page 122.

Igneous rock came first of course, since there was nothing else at the beginning of earth's history, and it is still being formed—as are the other rock types. The igneous rocks can be broadly divided into acidic (light coloured) and basic (dark coloured), each with its own set of typical mineral ingredients. Granite is the most familiar of all the acid rocks. The minerals of granite come mostly from the quartz and feldspar bins. An added spoonful of mica, tourmaline or garnet, and perhaps a pinch of zircon or topaz, would make a standard granite cake.

The dark igneous rocks such as gabbro and basalt require generous measures of amphiboles, pyroxenes and olivine as well as plagioclase feldspars. The orthoclase and microline feldspars do not figure in recipes for the dark rocks; quartz is also absent. But certain oxides of titanium (rutile, brookite, ilmenite) may be present as seasoning. A group of silicates called zeolites are of particular interest to collectors, since they are to be found in basaltic and similar rocks, and when well formed in large cavities can be very handsome specimens. But more of these in the next chapter.

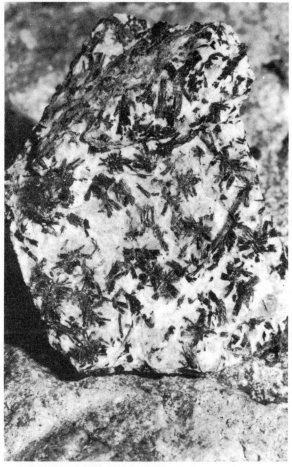

Amphiboles. **Above** *Crystallized (uncommon) glaucophane from Sierra Nevada, California—closely related to crocidolite* **(top right)** *.* **Top** *Crocodolite asbetos (the fibres seen in tiger-eye) from Australia.* **Centre** *Actinolite, dark green 'splinters' in schist, from the Alps.* **Above** *Actinolite from Norway.*

The **pyroxene-amphibole** groups (sometimes called 'pyroboles' in exasperation) are quite confusing to the average collector, since they are apt to look alike and individual species of one group often have echoes in the other. Augite (pyroxene) and hornblende (amphibole) in particular are both likely to occur as stubby black crystals. Of the two jade minerals, nephrite is an amphibole while jadeite is a pyroxene. The key to the group to which a 'pyrobole' mineral belongs is in its cleavage. Pyroxene has two cleavages, nearly at right angles; amphiboles' two cleavages are at acute and obtuse angles (56° and 124°) to each other.

Wollastonite, a pyroxene from the metamorphic rock of Meldon Quarry (see page 12).

Metamorphic rocks have a much bigger variety of ingredients to draw upon, and the recipes tend to be correspondingly flexible. Some consist almost entirely of mica, chlorite, tourmaline or garnet. Others may be almost pure calcite in the form of marble (metamorphosed limestone). Varying measures of garnet, axinite, epidote and idocrase (which are occasional ingredients of igneous rocks) may be added. The triplets kyanite, sillimanite and andalusite (chemically identical aluminium silicates, but physically different) are strictly metamorphic minerals.

Top left Clove-brown axinite from Meldon Quarry.
Top right Andalusite from Brittany. **Above** Twinned
stauxolite crystals, called 'fairy crosses', from
Brazil.

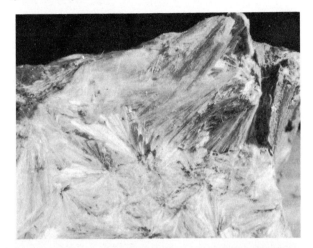

Left Pistachio-green epidote crystals from Baja California. *Below* Sillimanite from India. *Bottom* Twinned crystals of blue kyanite from Brazil. *Opposite page, top* Andalusite, variant chiastolite, showing the cross in section. *Bottom* Picrolite, a fibrous serpentine.

Sedimentary rocks are much less promising as sources of minerals than igneous or metamorphic. Sometimes older sedimentaries, such as Carboniferous limestones, may have had mineralisation in the form of ore veins injected into them, but the newer ones are only likely to contain those which form in 'cool' conditions and are deposited from solutions seeping through the rock. Typical minerals of this type are calcite, dolomite and aragonite (especially in limestones), gypsum, baryte, celestine; the iron minerals pyrite, marcasite, hematite, goethite and siderite. Flint, chalcedony and agate may also form as nodules in chalk, clay and other similar rocks. Unlikely though it may seem, silica can be suspended in water and carried along until it meets the nucleus of a nodule of its own kind to which it can cling. In fact, minerals found in recent sedimentary rock are frequently in the form of nodules, but except for calcite and dolomite (in limestone), they are incidental to the rocks, and not rock-forming.

One type of mineral has not been mentioned so far for a number of reasons; for one thing, it is a small group occurring in restricted conditions. In many cases it overlaps other groups—the spars in particular. The one thing these minerals have in common is that they were all deposited from a solution in water, by evaporation. Salt (halite) and gypsum are the most striking examples. Their many massive deposits are an important factor in man's economy. In the case of salt, which is far more soluble in water than gypsum, it normally exists in conditions of very low humidity, such as arid deserts, or underground, away from weathering or subterranean waters, although salt pans, fed by sea water evaporated by a hot sun, also exist on a smaller scale. Other highly soluble minerals exist in the right conditions. Copper sulphate (chalcanthite) is a good example. In fact if it were not so soluble it would undoubtedly be quite common, since the conditions for its formation are not lacking. Another sulphate, that of magnesium, is better known as Epsom Salts (epsomite).

The large deposits of salt are mostly the result of the drying up of sea water. The great inland lake deposits may produce various minerals other than halite. Of particular importance are the deposits of borate minerals such as colemanite, ulexite, kernite and, of course, borax. They all tend to be whitish and translucent, and most are soluble in water and must be kept away from humidity. Borax as a commercial product of these minerals is used as an ingredient in fertilisers, soaps and antiseptics, cosmetics, in gasoline fuel, and in the manufacture of steel, to mention just a few of its applications. The greatest boron deposits in the world are concentrated in California and Nevada, the site of the famous Death Valley, as well as in Turkey.

Another product of evaporation (or evaporite) is trona, a natural carbonate of soda. It sometimes forms crusts on the surface of lakes, as in the Fezzan in Libya.

Opposite page Minerals from soft sedimentary rocks: a septarian nodule, its fissures coated with calcite and rosettes of barite crystals, with, left to right, a pyrite nodule, a concretion, an agate, a gypsum sand-rose and calcite crystals.

Below left Pyrite nodules and **below right** marcasite crystals from chalk. **Bottom** Evaporates from California, **left to right**: gaylussite, inderite (front), ulexite (back) borax.

Gemstones

This brings us to those minerals which unquestionably have the widest appeal, the gemstones. While these are to be found in every major chemical group, the silicates have something approaching a monopoly, and many rock-forming silicates may on occasion blossom into the glamorous varieties we know as gemstones. From the light-coloured igneous rocks there are beryl (aquamarine and emerald), topaz, tourmaline and zircon (also amethyst, citrine and the other crystalline quartzes, if you regard quartz as a silicate). The dark igneous rocks are less productive, but include olivine (peridot) and some that are less widely known as gemstones such as augite, diopside, and plagioclase (labradorite). The metamorphic rock-formers are represented by garnets, kyanite, sphene, precious serpentine, jade and others.

The better known gemstones remaining are diamond (the element carbon), ruby and sapphire (both from the oxide corundum), spinel and chrysoberyl (also oxides) and turquoise (a phosphate).

There is nothing specifically which marks a gemstone from a pretty mineral or rock. The term is a loose one intended to cover any stone which can be considered for use in jewellery. The truly precious stones (the so-called 'noble' gemstones) are limited to diamond, ruby, sapphire and emerald. Each has the qualities most needed in a gem to a marked degree, that is, a brilliant lustre, durability and good colour. Although diamond is typically without colour it easily makes up for this by its brilliant fire and lustre. Emerald, sapphire and ruby each lend their names to describe a particularly rich green, blue and red. Diamond is the hardest natural substance by a good margin, ruby and sapphire (mineralogically the same

Botryoidal chalcedony. Black when found, this specimen was cleaned with oxalic acid.

as corundum) are second only to diamond in hardness, with emerald (a very green beryl) coming a close third. So much for their durability. Topaz, zircon, garnet and amethyst are all hard, and can be cut and facetted well. Other stones, fluorite for instance, are clear and attractively coloured and will polish well, but will not stand up to any wear and so are not in favour for use as gems.

Others, best described as decorative or ornamental stones, include serpentine, various marbles and granites, 'Blue John' (a banded blue and white or amber variety of fluorite), banded malachite and rhodochrosite, unakite (a rock composed of green epidote and pink feldspar) and many more. Jade, turquoise, and lapis lazuli, although used in carving for ornaments and objects d'art, rank higher than mere ornamental stones owing to a certain rarity and their fine colour.

The silica minerals are in a class by themselves when it comes to gemstones. In the first place, as members of the largest family in the mineral kingdom gathered under the name of one species (quartz), they are the work horses of the lapidary world. Many are simply well coloured specimens of crystal quartz, citrine (yellow), amethyst (purple), morion (black) and rose quartz, for instance. Cairngorm is a smoky to yellow brown variety coming from the Cairngorm mountains of Scotland. All these can be cut and facetted to bring out the natural sparkle.

Another side of the quartz family is known as micro-crystalline, because it never shows its crystal structure to the unaided eye. Its members are translucent rather than transparent, the head of this branch being chalcedony. The names come from the colours or, in some cases, from the patterning.

An attractive specimen of amber-coloured opal containing pyrolusite dendrites from Hungary.

Chalcedony is usually in light muted colours, smoky blues, straw yellow and so on. The orange-yellow to red varieties are better known as carnelian, sometimes spelt cornelian; both are correct (carne = flesh, corne = horn, from the colours). Prase (soft leek-green), chrysoprase (clear grass-green) and sard (brown) are also chalcedony varieties. The various agates are simply multi-coloured chalcedonies whose patterning may be of an almost endless variety, the most familiar being in the form of concentric, uneven rings. Onyx is a kind of agate in which the colours are formed in flat layers (which appear as straight lines when cut across the 'grain'), a fact which is utilised in carving some cameos. There is also a greenish type of banded marble which is sometimes called onyx, but should not be confused with the real thing. Opal also belongs to the silica family.

While most precious stones are established and well known, new ones are still being discovered. Brazilianite, a yellow-green phosphate discovered in Brazil in 1944, is one of the latest to join this select band. Every so often, discoveries are made of specimens of well-known minerals, not previously thought of as gemstones, but of a quality and colour which warrants their description and use as such. So it is almost impossible to draw a line between everyday minerals and their elegant brothers with pretensions to the 'nobility'.

Some varieties of silica. **Above** *An 'agate rose', a concretion of chalcedony from Brazil.* **Opposite page, top left** *Tiger-eye, (silica enveloping crocidolite asbestos).* **Centre, bottom left & right** *Quartz crystal—normal, slender and stumpy.* **Top right** *Aggregate of quartz crystals showing a secondary deposit of a dark mineral on upper surfaces, indicating direction from which the solution carrying it came.*

Where they come from

I can remember, as a small child, looking through my mother's jewellery box and being very much attracted to the garnets, amethysts and particularly to a string of carnelian beads. Inevitably, I wanted to know where they came from in the first place, and equally inevitably the answer was vague and unsatisfactory to the relentless curiosity of the young. The thought that precious stones could actually be found and picked up by ordinary mortals without the assistance of genii or magic lamps was stimulating, to say the least, but it was frustrating to be told that one must travel to distant countries with horrible climates, endure the attentions of lions and tigers, snakes and scorpions, and then have to dig enormous holes in the earth to reach them. It would have been much more convenient to be able to go and grub around in the back garden. If only I had known,

there was probably a modest haul of jasper to be had right there, but I would not have recognised it as such unless it had been pointed out to me.

Gemstones in nature have a way of not showing their true colours, in both senses of the phrase. A relatively common stone like jasper has very little of interest or value until it is actually cut and polished. The heart of a big city like London is not the sort of place you would expect to be able to look for raw gems, but in amongst the ubiquitous gravel of that city, small, dull red pebbles may be found which are in fact composed of jasper. Not the best quality jasper by a long way, it must be admitted, but good enough to take an excellent polish in a tumbler (to be described later), and look quite pretty on a piece of home-made jewellery.

Typical chalk quarry of south-eastern England, with lime kilns—the home of flint and pyrite nodules.

Geology

The point of all this is that minerals and gemstones are everywhere around you and under your feet. The rock where they originate may be a few feet down under the pavement, or twenty feet down under soil, or a hundred feet under the river mud. The best ones are unlikely to be right at hand and will probably take time and effort to find. As will already be apparent, the right place to look for one type will probably be quite the wrong place to look for another, and this is directly linked to geology. So it is obvious that for a serious pursuit of mineral collecting in the field, a basic understanding of geology is important.

To take the landscape itself for a start: the *shape* of it will give a clue to the type of rock on which it is based. The topsoil and even the vegetation (if any) can also be a guide, since the soil and the type of growth it encourages are directly derived from the surrounding rock. For instance, a very flat, low-lying landscape implies rock of recent sedimentary origin (although basaltic flows may also be flat). Rock of volcanic or other igneous types, on the other hand, are usually associated with wild, often bleak terrain with the rocky bones showing through in places. Old limestone country has a stern character of its own, often cavernous, while chalk downs are recognised for their gentle, rolling grandeur. Very ancient hills, even of granite, are usually softened and fertile, however harsh they may once have been. Taking these few elementary examples a number of possible minerals for each area can be suggested.

In the case of your low-lying plain, the rock to expect will be alluvial, perhaps sandy or clayey. (Rock in the geological sense includes non-hard material such as clay, or loose gravel.) Interesting minerals are likely to be very few, or very small. Gold dust is found in alluvial sand and gravel, but usually in the context of a river cutting through gold-bearing rock. It should be mentioned here that where there is gravel resulting from glacial deposits, you may be dealing with an assortment of fragments which originated hundreds of miles away and have little or no relation to each other. Here you have a sort of lucky dip, with nothing to guide you but chance.

An old photograph of Botallack tin and copper mine, still good for collecting.

Sedimentary rock that has had a little longer to consolidate may have accumulated some interesting mineral nodules, such as flint or chalcedony, with the possibility of gemstone pebbles like carnelian or agate. Crystals of gypsum (selenite) or baryte are not infrequently found in these conditions, as are crystals and nodules of pyrite and marcasite (for example, in chalk). On the whole the most interesting finds in such rock are likely to be fossils, but these are outside the scope of this book.

Chalk is for the most part limited to flint nodules and occasional pyrite nodules, and we must look to the older limestones for a more promising field for study. Calcite crystals are the best bet here, with dolomite, aragonite and quartz as runners up. Where mineral veins have been injected into or replaced limestone, we can look amongst others for fluorite and baryte as gangue, and for galena and sphalerite as ores.

The rough landscape of granite or basalt will have the promise of minerals associated with the particular rocks involved. As seen in the previous chapter, granite goes with a definite set of minerals, many of which are of special interest to collectors.

Particularly sought after is a granitic type of rock called pegmatite. The exact reasons for the existence of pegmatite and how it forms are still not completely understood, so we will leave this to the experts and confine ourselves to what pegmatites are. This form of rock is sometimes called 'giant granite', owing to the size of crystallisation of its constituent minerals. It usually takes the form of 'dykes' or veins cutting through large masses of ordinary granite. Pegmatites may consist only of smallish lens-shaped bodies, or may take up most of a mountain. Although one may have pegmatites of dark igneous rocks, the word usually refers to the light-coloured or granite types, where the most interesting ones are found. The minerals are the usual ones of granite type: quartz, feldspar and mica, and often tourmaline. Where there are cavities, these will crystallise, often handsomely. But what is more exciting for the collector is the fact that much rarer minerals, including several gemstones, may also crystallise inside these cavities.

The huge pegmatites of Brazil have produced many of the world's finest specimens of quartz, tourmaline, topaz and beryl, along with less familiar but no less attractive minerals. Similar to pegmatites, but smaller, are the open pockets found in some granites called miarolitic cavities. These also may contain crystallised granite-pegmatite minerals, an example of which is shown here, with a fine specimen of aquamarine (beryl) from the Mountains of Mourne.

Slieve Binnian in the Mourne Mountains, Ireland. Cavities in granite contain topaz, beryl, etc.

Basalt scenery in Iceland, where many fine zeolite specimens are to be found.

Some pegmatite specimens. **Top** *A complex group of crystals including quartz, feldspar, tourmaline crystals (some hair-like), china clay and fluorite.* **Opposite page, top** *Free-standing feldspar crystals with quartz, mica and tourmaline; also loose* crystals: smoky quartz, black tourmaline and biotite mica. **Above left** *Long prisms of tourmaline in quartz.* **Above right** *Stumpy tourmaline crystals.* **Bottom right** *Mica from pegmatite.*

Dark igneous rocks may be less rewarding than the lighter-coloured ones, with some notable exceptions. There are, particularly among basalts, rocks which may contain innumerable cavities ranging in size from that of a pea or less to that of a grapefruit or larger. These cavities (sometimes called amygdales from the Greek for almond), are gas bubbles trapped in the cooling lava, and usually become filled with certain minerals. Under some conditions, silica solutions will seep into the bubbles, forming nodules of agate. These hard plums in the basalt cake will often remain intact when the less durable basalt has weathered away, and become loose pebbles ready for the lucky gemhunter to pick up. Under other circumstances, they may fill with other minerals, the most attractive being that group of silicates known as zeolites.

Although rarely well coloured and inclined to be without much lustre, zeolites crystallise readily in a number of forms which contrast pleasantly with each other, since it is characteristic for two or more to be found on the same specimen. The word zeolite comes from the Greek for 'to boil', owing to its most distinctive characteristic, which is to swell and bubble when strongly heated, because of the high water content.

Some zeolites. **Above** Cubelike crystals of white chabazite in a basalt cavity. **Top** Small pink chabazite crystals with 'sheaves' of brown stilbite crystals. **Above right** Apophyllite crystals found in association with zeolites.

114

A fine group of natrolite prisms and analcime trapezohedrons.

Top Basalt cliffs in Northern Ireland. **Above** A road
cutting in Scotland—a good place to stop. White
veins could mean specimens.

Examples of mineralisation in basaltic rocks can be found in two types from Scotland. Fairly recent basalts, from the Tertiary period of geology, occur in several parts of the Highlands and the Western Isles. They are often rich in zeolite-filled cavities. A much older basalt, penetrating the Devonian rocks of the midland valley, are the source of agates so abundant as to be called 'Scottish Pebbles' when found in nearby beaches and river beds.

Man-made workings

Wherever man has had a foothold on the face of the earth he has left behind signposts of all kinds, from shallow burrowings and earth heaps to the strange-looking ruins of old mine workings, which say 'Here be riches of the earth'. A first trip through the length of Cornwall, can be a haunting experience for anyone who thought he knew his Britain. In most places there are the familiar villages and cosy valleys, but elsewhere there is a desolation suggestive of craters on the moon. Around the centre of the peninsula there is a weird stretch of landscape peppered with conical white mountains and matching conical pits. In lonely and improbable places one finds those gaunt ruins that are more likely to evoke thoughts of Cornish giants and ogres than the memories of the pioneering engineers of steam power, Newcomen, Watt and Trevithick, whose brain children they once housed. The white mountains are, of course, waste from china clay pits (often wryly described as the 'Cornish Alps') and are but one of many of the signposts of mineral wealth so common in Cornwall.

The remarkable honeycomb structure of the Giant's Causeway basalt (Northern Ireland), caused by shrinkage of cooling lava.

A disused copper mine in sandstone. The vein was worked from the surface downwards — still good for collectors, Alderley Edge. Cheshire, England.

It is one thing to know what minerals to expect in a given area and quite another thing to get at them. One cannot go around digging holes in the ground hoping to run across interesting nodules, let alone blast open exposures of granite on the off-chance of finding a good pegmatite. And it stands to reason that any minerals on the surface will usually be weathered beyond recognition or have been collected by some Palæolithic rockhound in 50,000 BC.

One must find exposures of recent origin. These can be natural or man-made. Of the first, the most likely places are cliffs and beaches, where nature is continually excavating itself. Likewise the beds of rivers and streams may be productive. Of a more drastic nature there are landslides, earthquakes and volcanoes, but these are not recommended for the beginner. Of those made by man, quarries and mines are the most promising, road and rail cuttings and tunnels may prove fruitful if the rock is of the right kind, but this is much more of a gamble. Nevertheless, some classic mineral specimens have come from these chance cuttings, such as quartz crystals from the Simplon Tunnel, and the discovery of the rare cadmium sulphide, greenockite, in a railway cutting near Glasgow, many years ago.

Quarries

A working quarry is certainly a most capricious place in which to collect, although many of the best specimens come from these. Quarry-men as a rule are looking for rock which is even-textured and free from the flaws where minerals are most likely to congregate. Sometimes a quarry may have to be abandoned because of an increasing number of pegmatites and vughs, in fact, just at the point where it starts to get really interesting for the collector. If the minerals are of sufficient value in themselves (feldspar, spodumene and beryl are sometimes worked for their mineral content), the quarrying will continue. Beryl, for instance, is a source of the element beryllium. If you have access to a quarry of this kind you are in luck. The old one at Branchville, Connecticut, is such a place, and even after being abandoned for years there are still pickings to be had, so abundant were the original minerals. But on the whole long-abandoned quarries are likely to be played out of samples worth taking home, for example, the Colcerrow quarry at Luxulyan and its beautiful apatite crystals. If, as in Brazil, the minerals are gemstones or of high specimen appeal, these are extracted for their own sake and collectors will then be obliged to buy them.

An old photograph of East Pool mine underground (see page 37 for engine house).

Mines

The dumps of old mines are the most popular with the average rockhound, since they are usually more accessible than those of working mines, but they lack the fresh material of the latter. On the other hand, modern mining methods, although economically more efficient, are less selective than the old, when everything was picked and dug away by hand. Some beautiful specimens from Victorian collections could hardly have survived a modern mining operation with its blasting and mechanical shovels. In those days, a miner could be sure of a ready buyer for any good specimens he could find. This was not, of course, encouraged by the mine owners. It is said of one small but particularly rich mine in Cornwall that more copper was bootlegged out to dealers in the form of specimens than went to the crushers, for which posterity at least should feel truly thankful. In a sense these miners were doing a job of conservation on natural resources which can never be replaced, although it is not likely that this was their first consideration.

Another point about mines: the minerals for which they operate are the least likely to be found on the waste dumps, for obvious reasons. It is the associated minerals of little or no commercial value to the mine that one finds. These are the crumbs for the collector. But there is still another angle to mine dumps. Very old ones, while much weathered on the surface, may yield surprisingly good material if one digs well down into them. This is because the older mining methods were often a bit prodigal of the ore, and much was thrown away as being insufficiently rich to bother with, or in some cases minerals of value were not recognised because they were not the ones being sought. Many a waste heap has been reworked profitably for these once discarded minerals.

Before leaving the subject of dumps it must be pointed out that much of the material in these is simply waste rock which was never in contact with mineral veins; and if one is not alert to the difference, a lot of time can be wasted in turning over completely barren 'junkite'. In short, collecting from old dumps may be rewarding for the patient, but frustrating for those who are not.

As for the inside of a working mine, one is very unlikely to do any collecting on the spot, and the nearest one is likely to get to the veins is on a formally conducted tour. On the other hand, one young rockhound I know became so obsessed with the idea of collecting on the spot that he got himself a job as a miner.

The insides of old mines are another matter. They may, of course, be extremely dangerous, and unless one is well equipped and briefed, and preferably in the company of an experienced spelunker or potholer, one should not attempt them. Nevertheless a lot of worthwhile material is to be had in some of them.

Other sites and areas

For those who would like to know where to look specifically for gemstones, there is no short answer, as will have been guessed by now. Some beaches may have agates, carnelians and amethysts. Pegmatites may contain topazes, beryls, amazonstones, tourmalines and quartzes. For diamonds one must go to one of the very few sites in the world where a certain volcanic rock known as kimberlite is found, and since all the worthwhile ones are well guarded, it would be a waste of time and money. Gravels in river beds are the classic sources of rubies, sapphires and other of the rarer gemstones, but the particular river beds are usually in remote corners of Asia, Africa, or South America.

Minerals, unlike organic species, have universal form. The general rule with flora and fauna is that even related species have quite localised distinctions. A field guide to the birds of Florida would be a bad buy in California, although both are on the same continent and have similar sub-tropical climates. On the other hand, a good mineral handbook is valid in any part of the world. It is always unwise, even for the experienced professional, to commit oneself too strongly to guessing a locality. A quartz crystal from Sweden is not by itself distinguishable from one from Lesotho or Sarawak. The reniform hematite or 'kidney ore' of Cumberland is certainly unmatched elsewhere, but the formation itself can be found in all parts of the world, and familiarity with one would make recognition of another automatic.

There are exceptions to this rule, especially where the specimen is in matrix. The combination can sometimes be a sort of trademark to the place of origin. The association of two or three minerals can suggest a place of origin as well as help to make identification easier. A good example of a place with a characteristic set of mineral associations is in the remarkable zinc mines of Franklin Furnace and Stirling Hill in New Jersey, USA.

The famous minerals of Franklin are red zincite, black franklinite and green to brownish willemite (all zinc minerals which in combination were the classic Franklin ore). Other well known minerals from there are rhodonite, magnetite, spinel, and phlogopite, all to be found in major collections.

Although these mines are now defunct and the great specimens are mostly tucked away in private or public collections, the very rich and extensive dumps of one (the Buckwheat mine) are still there, and happily they are still open to visiting rockhounds, for whom they have become something of a mecca. A remarkable feature of Franklin is the number of minerals reported, many of which are rare or unique. Another aspect for which it is famous are the fluorescent minerals, and no collection of these is complete without the Franklin classic of brilliant green willemite in rich pink calcite – all the more dramatic because of its lack of colour in ordinary light.

This isolated and unique outcrop of zinc ore is quite different from the mineralisation of, say, the zinc-producing mines of Cornwall. In fact, mining here was so dominated by copper and tin that the production of arsenic antimony, iron, silver, lead, zinc and tungsten, amongst others, went almost unnoticed. The zinc occurrence was mostly the conventional one of sphalerite in association with galena. (At Franklin, sphalerite was not common enough to be counted as an ore.)

Mineralisation in Cornwall is remarkable for its variety of species (around 300) and for the number of rare ones, especially among the coppers. Even the tired old dumps will yield up new species every now and then, and with the recent new lease of life to tin mining, the end is not yet in sight. Cornwall has the added attraction of a coastline with several gemstone beaches (a guide to finding these is mentioned in the reading list on page 143), and a varied geology to match the wide range of mineral types.

These two classic areas are quoted for contrast, and from first-hand experience. Other classic collecting areas around the world often vary more sharply in character even than these examples.

Many of the famous localities are hardly places for the humble rockhound, being too remote or restricted, but often provide a living for dealers in gemstones and specimens. When one talks airily of Minas Gerais in Brazil one means a province about the size of Texas. While North America is certainly a rockhound's paradise – with Australia a close second, particularly for those who like the sound of prospecting for gemstones – Europe is less so. Many of the classic European sites are being built upon or close to free-lances, perhaps justifiably in some cases. African sites are often remote and rockhunting is not especially encouraged. In Asia, where the gem trade is very ancient, there is an understandable reluctance to reveal sources or encourage what might seem like outsiders' competition.

Some of the best collecting grounds around the world are, however, becoming available to rockhounds with a little fat in their bank accounts. This is because organised collecting holidays and charter flights are becoming increasingly popular, particulars of which are advertised from time to time in the appropriate magazines. The USA leads the way here, not only with well-organised outings and tours in every part of the country, but also collecting holidays in Canada, Mexico and South America.

In the meantime, it is more practical to begin by enjoying the pleasures at hand. After all, one will approciate that global rockhunt all the more when it comes. So in the next chapter we will have a closer look at how to go about it in our own back-yards.

The hobby in the field

There is nothing new about collecting minerals, but whereas primitive man probably needed some kind of reason for doing so, such as a belief in magical properties or as some kind of status symbol, the more advanced civilizations produced a different kind of collector. We know that in classical times rocks and minerals were studied for their own sakes and often the guesses as to their origin were very close to the mark. Of course, the belief that quartz crystals were actually ice which had frozen so hard that it could not be melted again was pretty wild, but in other ways writers such as Pliny and Theophrastus were able to describe minerals well enough for us to recognise them, even though the names they used were different from the ones we know.

It would be nice to think that Herodotus, who in the fourth century BC wrote some of the first known records of minerals, had his own rock collection. Is it too much to imagine him travelling from Athens to the lead mines at nearby Laurium (the modern Lavrion)–still one of the world's classic collecting sites–to grub around the waste heaps for unusual-looking lead minerals? At any rate it is something which has appealed to philosophers of all periods, using the term philosopher in its broadest and original sense. After the decline and fall of the ancient civilizations of Greece and Rome, there was not much call for such luxuries as pure science, and it is in an atmosphere of pure science that the rockhound is most likely to thrive. With the end of the dark ages and the dawn of the ages of 'reason' and 'enlightenment' there came both the leisure and

A collecting Mecca—Buckwheat Mine dump. Franklin, New Jersey, USA. The zinc mines are defunct, but fluorescent and other rare minerals may still be found there.

inclination to make natural history collections and study them for their own sake. The eighteenth century saw the advent of volumes, carefully illustrated with engravings of all kinds of natural phenomena. Those of Philip Rashleigh and James Sowerby are typical examples.

Early mineral collections have one especial advantage over most other kinds of collection, in that most mineral specimens are unusually durable and, if properly treated, may be as fresh after a hundred years as on the day they were found. Philip Rashleigh's own superb collection, the greater part of which is now the pride of Truro Museum in Cornwall, offers a good example. Original specimens, from which the engravings for his books were drawn, are still around. A few of Rashleigh's specimens found their way into the collection of an equally famous mineralogist of the twentieth century, the late Sir Arthur Russel. This was passed on to the British Museum at his death and some of the best of these have a case to themselves in the mineral gallery of the Natural History department in South Kensington, London.

The eighteenth and nineteenth centuries were a peak period for the dilettante gentleman-philosopher. It was a time when it was possible for one person to be able to hold in his head the essence of all knowledge available to his age. Collecting minerals was not, for him, a specialist hobby but a means to an end: knowing and understanding nature in its entirety. John Ruskin (1819–1900) was too busy to be called a dilettante, but when he was not being a poet, art critic and sociologist, or lecturing on history, architecture, drawing and economics, he put together a personal collection of 'curiosa' which has now become a museum at Coniston in the Lake District, much of it taken up with his mineral collection.

The nineteenth century was a peak period for mineral dealers. In Britain, there was a mining boom, the scale of which is hard to believe today. About 1860, Cornwall and Devon alone produced 40% of the world's copper, while in 1870, the area was producing half the world's tin! Lead mining, particularly in Derbyshire, was on a scale not far short of this. Specimens of minerals were being produced which will never be repeated and, fortunately for posterity, these were eagerly sought after and lovingly preserved. Europe was the main scene of this activity in the early part of the century, since the search for minerals had naturally begun in the backyard of the industrial revolution.

Today, dealers who were once directly involved with seeking and finding their wares are now more likely to depend on the remote control of modern communications, as new classics are being turned up in more remote parts of the world, which will eventually join the ranks of the unattainable. But the do-it-yourself aspect of collecting has correspondingly spread. The pleasure of finding and recognising your own specimens far outweighs the fact that few of them would be worth bequeathing to a museum.

The hunt

Few genuine rockhounds would be put off visiting a famous old site by the knowledge that generations before him had gone over it with fine-tooth combs. To find one miserable fragment of a mineral for which it was famous is enough–anything more is heaven! The hunt is the thing, and a shining faith in one's own luck which will lead one to the single fantastic specimen which has eluded a thousand other pairs of eagle eyes. And what keeps one going, in spite of frustrations and disappointments, like an inveterate gambler, is the occasional lucky strike.

One of the most satisfying aspects of mineral collecting in the field is that it provides an objective for an expedition which might otherwise never have been made, but which, once completed, would not have been missed for worlds. One discovers out of the way corners whose existence was never suspected; more often than not, they are attractive for their own sake, because many forms of mineralisation coincide with the earth movements which provide so much dramatic scenery.

This does not mean that all mineral sites are off in the wilds, nor does it mean that all the good ones are in beauty spots. Some of my best finds, have been made around the gloomy ruins of long-dead mines, but if beauty is in the eye of the beholder, even these waste lands can have a stark, romantic appeal of their own.

Like all treasure hunting, the final outcome of a rockhunt can not be known until the last moment. On one occasion, I found my best specimen of the day getting into the car to leave the scene: it would not have been noticed at all if I had not carelessly dropped the car keys on top of it. On another day, I had combed the extensive dumps of Wheal Basset, an old Cornish copper mine, picking up various nondescript pieces of blue and green secondary copper minerals–mostly malachite and chrysocolla and some cuprite crystals. The site is a recognised one for torbernite, but I had only found traces of this. Finally, it was time to call it a day, chiefly because the twilight was turning to night and green could barely be distinguished from brown. I had mentally thrown in the towel on the days exertions, when a greenish patch caught my eye a few yards away, across the steep and slippery bank, looking more like moss than a mineral. Aching legs and common-sense dictated a dignified acceptance of the principle that enough is enough, but that is not the way of your diehard rockhound. In short, the final scramble of the day was rewarded with a group of torbernite crystals worthy of a place in any collection. How this had remained undetected for several decades without being discovered by one of the countless collectors who have roamed the area over the years is a mystery. My guess is that it had been covered by a layer of dirt which had gradually been washed away by rain.

Most quarries will turn up the odd mineral specimen at intervals, while many will produce a regular trickle which usually makes the casual visit rewarding. It all depends upon the 'luck of the blast'. If you arrive at the scene soon after recent blasting you will have first pick of anything the dynamite may have turned up, and if you do not take what you find, the chances are the material will probably all end up in the crusher before the next collector comes along.

The bonanza days are often the result of fate being in a festive mood. For instance, there was a small granite quarry in Cornwall I had read about in an article, written some twenty years earlier, describing a most interesting pegmatite occurrence which had been noted there. Tracking down the exact site proved to be difficult, as there was a number of quarries in the neighbourhood which answered the description. It was not until some months after first starting the search that another collector and I stumbled on the correct one. Sure enough the pegmatite material was there, lying around in great chunks

after a recent blasting. There was not only enough for both of us, but specimens for years of trading. It was an occasion to break the rule of 'leave some for others', because this particular exposure would soon have been swallowed up in quarrying operations.

In frustrating the earlier attempts to find the place, fate had really been on our side. If I had found it first go, the pegmatite would not yet have been reached and we would have written off the site as played out. A few weeks and a couple of visits later, nothing was left to collect. This happened six years ago from the time of writing and no further exposures have been reported.

Different parts of the world can present different faces to the rockhound. There may be legal obstacles to overcome in one place and geological or topographical obstacles in another. Local geology has an important influence on one's approach, and different countries will breed different types of rockhound. In North America, one has the combination of a large variety of mineral locations, with the sort of freedom of movement and leisure time that is essential for making the best of them. In Europe, the situation is potentially the same except that the much denser population and the earlier working of minerals has tended to strip what resources there are. Australia,

Pegmatite fragment from the quarry mentioned on this page. Crystals include tourmaline, quartz and fluorite (at top).

Opal mining at White Cliffs, New South Wales. Australia is the opal centre of the world, and this is only one of many locations where they are mined. Equally well-known are Coober Pedy and Lightning Ridge. The picture **left** shows an old-timer operating a winch at a shaft which probably goes down 15 or 20 feet, where the richest layers may be found. The old 'mullock heaps' in the view **below**, like giant gopher holes, stretching as far as the eye can see, speak for themselves. Today, mining is still carried on by the pros, but visiting rockhounds are free to 'fossick' on the dumps which may contain respectable opals overlooked by the miners in their hurry to find bigger ones.

on the other hand, seems to be something of a rockhound's paradise, with virgin territory still to be explored. Here the emphasis is on a sort of prospectors' free-for-all. The spirit of the Forty-niners is still alive in the men who dig for opals at Coober Pedy and Lightning Ridge. Nearly every gemstone in the book is there for the taking if you have the time, the transport, and the determination.

Getting down to essentials

How does one go about looking for minerals and what equipment does one need? To start with the tools of the trade, there are two which are almost indispensable. One must have a good hammer ($1\frac{1}{2}$–2 lb) of the geologist's type and a magnifying glass of about ×10 power. The first is to break open specimens in order to get at the unweathered interior. The second is important for identification purposes, and will often open up a wonderland of tiny formations which would otherwise be missed. The value of these two is only too apparent if one finds oneself in a good location without them.

A tough canvas bag and lots of newspaper are also necessary for carrying your finds and wrapping them up for protection. This matter of protecting specimens is especially important, and when dealing with soft minerals like fluorite, calcite and gypsum it is vital. There is nothing more frustrating than to collect good crystals of these only to discover on getting them home those disfiguring chalky edges and corners, the result of rubbing together which has happened in transit, and could have been prevented with a little wrapping up in paper. A good protective tissue – with an alternative use in cases of emergency – is provided by a roll of 'softy' toilet paper. It is heartbreaking when one comes across the occasional old collection, the heirs to which have dumped everything together in cardboard boxes. Not only are there specimens invariably separated from vital labels, but are, except for the tougher ones like quartz, usually damaged to the point of uselessness.

Next to consider, in equipping oneself, is suitable protective clothing. Sturdy boots, gardening gloves (handling some rocks can be hard on the skin) and goggles to protect the eyes from flying chips during hammering operations, are all recommended, particularly the latter. If you are likely to be working near cliffs or in quarries, a helmet of some kind may be the difference between a carefree rockhunt and shortened outing and a bad headache, or even worse.

In my early days of rock hunting, I had stopped at a well-known quarry in New Jersey to try my luck. It was Saturday afternoon and the only people there were two other rockhounds, one of whom was halfway up one wall of the quarry, hacking away happily at a vugh full of calcite crystals. I wandered over to see what he was doing, looking around on the ground at the same time in case there was anything to be found there. Suddenly I heard a warning shout,

and simultaneously the quarry went dim and I was aware of a peculiar numbness in the region of my scalp. The other rockhound was naturally very much abashed and came scrambling down to help. He had broken one of the cardinal rules of collecting – never throw rocks if you do not look where they are going.

Half an hour later I felt able to leave; with some nice calcite crystals in the back of the car, a bump on the head protected by an old golfing cap and a slug of gin under my belt, all of which had been supplied by the errant and contrite rockhound.

There are many other items which can increase the chances of a successful rockhunt. Cold chisels for freeing specimens from rock masses, a light sledgehammer for breaking open boulders (assuming you have a car), a surplus trenching tool for digging into dumps, boxes to pack your finds in, maps, a notebook and any available guide to sites. Elementary testing equipment, penknife, copper coin and glass (for hardness, a magnet and a streak-plate are also advisable.

To prepare oneself for an expedition, it is necessary first of all to know the sort of territory which is available. If one lives in a mineralised area, one's collecting can be done on odd evenings in the summer, or even during a lunch hour, but for most people an expedition usually means a journey of an hour or two, or more. If it is done on holiday, you either pick your spot for the usual reasons of family convenience, scenery, camping or hotel amenities, probable weather, and hope to be within striking distance of a site or two; or you frankly head for the most promising area for minerals and hope the amenities are there. Fortunately for rockhounds with families not as keen as they are, the two often go together.

There is a number of sources you can consult, local rock clubs obviously being the best. If you belong to one of these at home, your local secretary should be able to put you in touch with the right person in the area. Subscribing to an amateur mineralogist's magazine is highly recommended as well, since it will usually contain all this sort of information, and often a rewarding trip to an otherwise unconsidered part of the country is inspired by one of its articles, or a reader's letter. Failing all this (and there are still many places left that are not to be found in the popular literature), contact the curator of the nearest museum or the geology department of a local college or university.

Having found out something about your territory and its minerals, the next step is to pinpoint your destinations by means of the best maps. In many places one can buy maps, such as the ordnance survey used in the British Isles, which use a standard reference grid. By using this one can be guided to any spot in the area covered simply by having a map number and a six-figure grid reference. I for one have wasted more time looking for some site off in the woods that is insufficiently described than I care to remember. The sort of direction that goes 'Take the fourth turning to the left after leaving Mac-Donald's farm going north, and a few hundred yards on the right there is a gate–' is useless. Often the writer does not seem to know north from south, left from right, or a yard from a furlong. MacDonald's farm is not on any map and nobody ever heard of him, the gate fell down and is covered with weeds. There is nothing like having an accurate map reference, and a compass, too.

Once you have found your quarry or mineworking or river-bed, the next consideration is what to look for and how. This is where experience is most valuable, and the advantage of being on a group outing with one or two old hands is greatest. Learning to look in the most likely places and recognising the most promising pieces to pick up is largely a matter of trial and error, and to some extent common-sense. Signs of previous collectors' activities can often be a help, and one soon learns to recognise these. The freshly-broken rock on top of a boulder (used as an anvil), the freshly-dug holes in a bank will suggest what to look for and where. Each site will have its own peculiarities which must be learnt first hand.

Look for rock that is different from its surroundings. Boulders with fissures and holes in them ask to be cracked open, as do large nodules. In the case of the latter, if they are known to contain crystals or formations, such as agate rings which are best enjoyed when sawn open, one must be patient until they can be properly cut. If you do not have the equipment, you can have them cut professionally for a small fee. Anything you do find of any worth should be most carefully protected from damage until you get home, and a note should be kept of what site they came from, and the date of the collection. In the case of large sites it is useful to note what part of it each specimen came from.

In some parts, it is not unusual to be able to visit several sites in one day. This is when labelling specimens on the spot is most important. A notebook is useful here for making observations for future reference, and many collectors augment their notes with photographs taken on the spot.

If you are looking for guidance in strange territory, a more intimate and pleasant way is to contact a local collector. Some of these will act as professional guides, in which case one can usually expect knowledgeable and expert assistance. When in a new area keep your eyes open for a rockshop. These are sure to be able to put you on to an enthusiast or guide, who is quite likely to be the proprietor himself.

Identification

The first thing one wants to know on finding a crystal or a colourful chunk of something new is what it is called. Of course some places are simply one-mineral sites and the problem does not arise.

In an opal-collecting area you know what you have got when you find it. The same goes for quartz crystals or agate. One soon learns to tell the difference between similar common minerals like quartz and calcite. Even if one is confused by an occasional similarity of crystal shape, one can usually recognise a difference in lustre. If this fails, the wide difference in hardness is conclusive. Your penknife will make no impression on the quartz, while on calcite it will leave distinct, chalky scratch marks. The use of a magnet is limited to those places where there is a chance of finding one of the two or three magnetic minerals. But if these are present a magnet is invaluable.

For sight identification, or 'eyeballing', experience is the only guide. Studying text books, photographic illustrations and specimens in collections is an essential step in learning, but it must not be forgotten that the specimen you found on the dumps of x-mine last week may look very different from the specimen of the same mineral from the same mine, presented to the museum in 1880. But one soon catches on to the commoner ones.

The next step in identification must wait until the return home. A rockhound is then likely to monopolise the kitchen sink for an hour or two, cleaning the dirt off his treasures. This must be done with some reserve on delicate, powdery minerals which might be destroyed, and not at all if there is any possibility of the minerals being soluble in water. Minerals freshly gleaned from a working quarry will almost certainly be dusty or muddy, and if mine or quarry mud is allowed to dry on calcite or dolomite crystals, the tiny fragments may stick permanently to the crystals and ruin their appearance. The ideal conditions for visiting a quarry are soon after blasting (for fresh exposures) and immediately after a torrential rainfall (to clean off some of the dust and show up good specimens by their wet surfaces). A wet day is, however, rather miserable and it prevents crystals from showing themselves by reflecting the sunshine.

When specimens are clean and dry, they can be examined again, and often minerals which had not been noticed in the field will suddenly become obvious. This can be the most exciting moment in the whole operation. Then, if there is still anything which has not been positively identified, you can make your lab tests. The idea of a home laboratory is not as daunting as it may sound. All one needs, apart from a few small items–test tubes, forceps, a charcoal block, a blowpipe, platinum wire in a holder–are a working surface, such as a kitchen table, a bunsen burner, and a few reagents (chemicals). Even the bunsen burner can be dispensed with and replaced with a blow torch, an alcohol lamp or even an ordinary candle. This equipment can be bought from most chemists. The purpose of it is to determine the effect of heat and active chemicals, such as acids, on small fragments of the mineral being analysed.

The platinum wire is used to hold a bead of molten borax in the bunsen flame, the borax containing a small amount of the mineral to be tested. The wire is made into a small loop, about 3 or 4 mm across, heated in the bunsen burner flame and quickly dipped into dry borax. Some of the borax will stick and, if heated again, will form a small colourless bead. A few grains of the mineral, having been pulverised with a pestle and mortar, are then touched with the red-hot molten bead. The powder picked up undergoes a chemical change with the borax, and if certain metals are present will, when reheated, show certain distinctive colours, depending on the part of the flame used and whether the bead is hot or cold.

For example, if copper is present in the sample, the bead will be green when hot; blue when cold if heated in the tip of the flame (the oxidizing part); colourless when hot and brown when cold if heated in the inner flame (the reducing part). The brown, on close inspection, turns out to be microscopic specks of natural copper. Most of the metals will give some quite positive colour reaction and this is one of the key methods of identifying their presence in a mineral. If more than one is present the bead will probably just go muddy, but other methods are available for sorting them out. The details will be found in the technical handbooks.

Other testing equipment

Ultra violet lamps ('black light') are not essential but, if the budget allows it, highly desirable. Most owners of UV lights are less interested in their use in identification than for the spectacular displays that a certain number of minerals (particularly the light-coloured uranium ores) will give under their lights. There are two kinds of these, long wave and short wave, which can now be bought in one unit. Portable UV lights can be used in the field, at night or under a tarpaulin in daylight. At places like Franklin, NJ, rich in fluorescent minerals, this equipment can sort the men from the boys, and make possible the finding of rare and otherwise inconspicuous minerals such as calcium larsenite (now renamed esperite).

Another piece of equipment, which is essential for a modern professional prospector, is a geiger counter. The scratchy sound that these make when exposed to radioactive material must be familiar to most, though a luxury for the average collector.

A recent arrival on the gadget scene is the metal detector, a commercialised mine detector in fact, much used by treasure hunters looking for old coins, but having some applications in the mineral collectors armoury.

There is another aspect of collecting which inevitably leads from one piece of equipment to another. If your most easily accessible localities are rich in gemstone pebbles, there will be an almost irresistible temptation to invest in a tumbler. A tumbler is a cylinder which can be the size of a jam jar or bigger than an oil drum. It is connected to machinery which makes it slowly revolve. Inside this one puts a mixture of pebbles (or gemstone chips), water, sawdust and an abrasive powder. The process is a refined variety of the one by which nature rounded her pebbles in the first place. By a series of changes of abrasive, the rough pebbles can first be smoothed, then polished to an almost mirror-like finish. The whole cycle can last a period measured in terms of months.

From here it is a short step to a diamond saw. This may even be more appealing, since the results are quick. If you have some agate pebbles which suggest an attractive internal marking, a saw will make a nice clean slice to reveal anything that may be there. Even when you have made your cut, the stone's potential is only half revealed. Not until the surface is polished will the whole richness of lustre, colour, translucency and so on be revealed. And this needs more equipment.

A lapping wheel, vaguely reminiscent of a record player turntable, is a rotating steel disc on which a series of grinding powders are placed to give progressively finer polishes to the piece of stone being worked. Another piece of equipment which is likely to be coveted is a set of grinding wheels, but from here one goes on to belt sanders, gem drills, vibro laps and even sphere cutters.

In certain areas, the variety of minerals is too limited to sustain very much interest, but some good pebble beaches can start one off on a cutting and polishing tack. And when local material begins to pall, a huge international network of dealers in gemstones can supply cheap cutting material from just about anywhere in the world, for you to cut, shape and polish to your hearts content.

Cataloguing and storing

The value of having a mineral's identification and place of origin firmly attached to it cannot be too strongly emphasised. The place of origin is the *only* thing that cannot be determined by instruments in the laboratory. If nothing else is with a specimen, this *must* be! A collection without these details can be almost worthless, while a carefully catalogued collection of well-selected minerals can be priceless.

The next thing is to see that they are properly protected, especially from dust, of which minerals are notoriously fond. If they are to be stored for easy reference, a set of suitably sized drawers is ideal, but if they are to be displayed a glass cabinet is essential. A glass-fronted book case is excellent, but the ideal is a case made especially for them, with glass on all sides and, if possible, strip lighting built in. Minerals need light to be fully enjoyed, particularly those with some degree of translucency or transparency. For these some kind of back lighting is best of all. The exception being, of course, the few minerals whose colour is affected by light, such as proustite and crocoite.

A mineral classic: stibnite crystals from Shikoku Island, Japan—a museum specimen about 2 feet from end to end.

tively complete collection. Buying your own allows an almost unlimited choice of subject.

Size is something to be considered at this stage. Those giant crystal groups, a foot or two across, normally seen only in museums or expensive shop windows, can be ruled out for a start. For one thing, the price of a specimen is partly governed by its weight – all other things being equal. If one simply wants to have a few minerals around as odd ornaments, the next size down (six inches to a foot) is to be recommended; while cabinet size, up to six inches, will fit into a drawer. Hand specimens and 'miniatures' are probably the most popular sizes, with 'thumbnails and micromounts' for those with limited space and a binocular microscope. All of which are regulated by size, for example, a micromount *must* fit into a one inch cube box.

Of the subjects to specialize in, a few are obvious, such as locality (one mine, one county, one country) ores (say, copper only), chemical class (phosphates, arsenates, silicates etc.) crystals (twinning, irregularities) and so on. Even individual species can offer endless variety. Calcite is a popular one because of the remarkable number of different crystal forms it can take. A collection of agates from around the world would offer plenty of scope. Even a collection of apatite crystals from different parts would allow a surprising variety of colour and formation. It is as well to remember that a theme like this will give interest to your display which a random hodge-podge, bought on impulse, may lack.

Although collecting things with an eye to selling them later at a huge profit is far from the spirit of the true collector, who would rather give his treasures to a worthy cause (such as a museum) than profit from them, it must be faced that it is widely practised. As with antiques and works of art, the demand is increasing at a greater rate than the supply. There will never be another mine producing the tetrahedrite and bournonite crystals exactly as found at Herodsfoot mine in Cornwall a hundred years ago. These, along with the stibnite crystals from Ichinokawa Shikoku Island, Japan, the franklinite–willemite–zincite specimens from Franklin Furnace, NJ, tourmaline from Elba, are classics which will never be repeated. To acquire good specimens of any of these is rather like trying to pick up an original Hogarth or Poussin. Even if your bank balance can take the strain you have to wait for the rare occasions when they come on to the market.

The administration side of many mining companies is not at all interested in conservation of any kind; either of the landscapes they may be disfiguring, or the irreplaceable crystals which may be shattered by dynamite or ground to powder in the crusher. They may even go so far as to dismiss any worker who tries to salvage specimens with a view to passing them on to collectors. This probably means that the future production of good specimens is likely to become increasingly lean, as methods for extracting ore become increasingly efficient and dehumanized. With the greater interest in mineralogy, and a more widespread awareness of the demand for good specimens, those in charge of such operations may perhaps find time to make some concessions to conservation in this area. To enlightened managers who set aside dumps for the benefit of collectors, and give aid and comfort in other ways, we should offer our heartfelt thanks.

Most active collectors, even those who specialize in their own finds, will be tempted from time to time to pay hard cash for a particularly attractive specimen; and many of the 'silver pick' specialists will, on occasion, try their luck with the hand-held kind. One of the most appealing ways of adding to a collection, and certainly well within the spirit of the game, is to barter. Most collectors in the field sooner or later run into a bonanza of sorts. When this happens they must strike a balance between being greedy, stripping everything in sight, leaving nothing for the next comer, and taking what they need for their own collections, and also laying in a stock of trading material.

What may seem like boring 'junkite' to one person, simply because his territory is saturated with it, can be a novelty in another area. I remember once seeing a piece of Kentish flint in a Pennsylvania rock-shop the kind of stuff they use for building walls, houses and churches with in south-east England. There was a respectable price on it, and the law of supply and demand could not have been better illustrated. Flint of that kind was unobtainable locally, not to mention the fact that it was labelled as coming from the White Cliffs of Dover.

Anyway, it is unlikely that one will be involved with minerals for long without making the acquaintance of other collectors. I have found that most rockhounds are unusually helpful, friendly and generous. Swapping seems to be a second nature to them and as you will often find yourself being presented with very nice pieces quite gratuitously, it is a good idea to have a stock from which to make your own donations. Exchanging by mail is another common practise. Here again one has the problem of goods sight-unseen, and variable standards of value, but it must be accepted as one of the risks of the game.

For the connoisseur with a cheque book, there is an interesting subject somewhere between minerals and man-made antiques. That is the field of artefacts in ornamental and precious stones. The first, probably, that comes to mind is Chinese jade, but this is only one of dozens of rock and mineral materials that have been used in this way: lapis lazuli, turquoise, rhodonite, malachite, nephrite, agate, onyx, carnelian and chalcedony among the more precious stones. Serpentine, alabaster, 'Blue John', fluorite, soapstone and various marbles are usually classed as ornamental and would not put such a heavy strain on the budget.

Four collectors' items. Brown calcite crystals from Sta. Eulalia, Mexico. blue azurite from Tsumeb, S–W Africa. pink erythrite from Australia, yellow adamite from Malpini, Mexico.

Barrel-shaped crystals of pyromorphite from Roughtongill, Cumberland, England.

Three rare lead minerals: left to right, vanadinite (lead vanadate) from Arizona, mimetite, variant campylite (lead arsenate) from Cumberland, pyromorphite (lead phosphate) from Cornwall.

Mineral classics

A thorough study of these and their sites around the world would make a book in itself, and there is only room here to look at a few of them. I have picked those which are the most generally sought-after because of their obvious eye-appeal, chiefly colour, lustre and crystal form, in that order.

Amethyst crystal groups Probably the most popular of all, since one is most likely to get value for money. The deepest purple is the most sought after, and although the price is geared to the quality of colour, there is enough around, particularly from Brazil, to keep the price within reason.

Citrine crystal groups The same mineral as amethyst, except for the yellow-brown colour. It is much rarer and correspondingly dearer. Since it can be created from amethyst by artificial heat treatment, much citrine which is sold as such is actually doctored amethyst, the nearest thing to forging a mineral you can get to. But the difference between this 'burnt sugar' citrine and the genuine article is not hard to tell. Most of the citrine today also comes from Brazil, but, as with amethyst, older specimens could have come from any of a dozen other parts of the world.

Rose quartz Another of the quartzes, is one of the few minerals which is acquired for its colour alone, regardless of form – which is usually non-existant anyway. Until recently, crystals were believed to be almost impossible to find but beautiful crystal specimens eventually turned up in Brazil, of course.

Rutilated quartz Yet another of the family, this one depends on needle-like inclusions of golden rutile for its appeal, sometimes romantically called 'Venus hairstone'. There is no room to go into details of all the crystal quartzes which make collector's items, but one should mention rock crystal, cairngorm and morion – most of which are found in Brazil but may come from about anywhere. Swiss smoky quartzes are highly prized – and highly-priced.

Agate geodes The old, famous locations in Germany, which made Idar-Oberstein, between the Mosel and the Rhine, the lapidary capital of the world, are somewhat depleted, but the industry still thrives, fed since 1827 from sources in Uruguay and Brazil. Mexico and Australia are also well known countries for agate.

Opal Usually considered too valuable as a gemstone to be found in private collections as display specimens, it is certainly handsome enough. Australia heads the list of occurrences, with Mexico coming second.

Tourmaline The wide range of colour, often mixed in one crystal, is part of the appeal. The crystals are nearly always in a white quartz matrix. Brazil again dominates the scene, but some of the finest crystals of all have come from California. A pink variety, known as rubellite, is sometimes found

A most unusual mineral, trona is a sesqui-carbonate of soda. It may form as a floating crust on the surface of lakes, also with evaporates in deserts (Kenya).

with lilac lepidolite, or with cookcite.

Dioptase Probably no mineral can match the deep rich emerald green of this copper silicate. Although specimens are usually crystallized, it is certain that the superb colour makes this one so sought after, and correspondingly costly. The original classic site for this was in the Kirghiz Steppe and the Ural Mountains, but now the best come from Tsumeb and Guchab in South-West Africa, and from the Congo (Zaire).

Malachite Another green copper mineral, it should be mentioned, for, besides its use in jewellery and as an ornamental stone in certain formations (notably botryoidal), it makes a handsome display specimen. In conjunction with azurite, it can be even more striking.

Azurite Closely linked with malachite, its deep royal blue is distinctive. Likely to be in crystals, which if well-formed puts up the price. Pseudomorphs of malachite after azurite crystals are especially good collector's items. Chessylite was the original name, after an old site in Chessy, France, where it was once found in quantity. Today most specimens of both malachite and azurite come from Tsumeb, S-W Africa; Katanga; Burra Burra, South Australia; Arizona, USA.

Sulphur Gives its name to a hue of yellow, and good crystals are becoming increasingly difficult to come by. Sicily was the classic area, the crystals being unusually large and often lustrous, but this is nearly played out, and prices are sky high. The specimen on page 20 is exceptional for its atypical amber yellow, and if one of these were to come on to the market you would be justified in paying the same sort of price as a piece of Ming porcelain would fetch. Small, bright yellow crystals are now being found in Baja California, Mexico.

Crocoite Like dioptase, sulphur, azurite and amethyst, this is an essential mineral for a collector who is using the colour spectrum for his theme. To green, yellow, blue and purple he can now add a most brilliant orange. The mineral is a lead chromate, and the splintery-looking crystals seen on page 129 are typical of the formation, but on a heroic scale, by ordinary collecting standards. This specimen was from the best of the known localities, Tasmania, but sadly, this is also in the past tense.

Proustite To round off the spectrum, it would be hard to find a more satisfactory red. Unfortunately, this is one of the least stable minerals from the colour point of view. In the unlikely event of being able to afford to buy a specimen, like the one on page 21, you would not be able to have it on display without losing the very colour which makes it so special. Exposed to light, it will acquire a metallic tarnish which robs it of the remarkable glowing translucence from which it gets the name 'Ruby Silver'. Our example is from the classic site, Chañarcillo, Chile.

Ruby (Corundum) A more permanent red can be represented by one of the several attractive occurrences. Best known is the one from Tanzania, with deep crimson crystals of thumbnail size embedded in emerald-green zoisite.

Fluorite One of the most collected of minerals because of the availability of good crystals with a wide colour range. Too common to quote every good source, but for colour and quality those of Cumberland, England, probably have the edge on most others. They are also fluorescent, and from them came the word itself. Large, well-coloured fluorites also come from the Tri-State district (the junction of Kansas, Oklahoma, and Missouri) and southern Illinois.

Copper The commonest of the naturally occurring metals may be found in the form of branching crystal groups. The classic site is a small peninsula in north-west Michigan, Keweenaw, where some of the largest and most interesting copper crystals have been found. So abundant were they that even modest collections are likely to have quite good specimens.

Other collector's favourites

The best calcite crystals on record are still those from the now barren mines of Cumberland. From the same part came the best 'kidney ore'. Zeolite groups make good collectors' pieces, and they may come from just about any part of the world you can mention, one of the most famous being the Watchung Mountains of Patterson, New Jersey. At the time of writing, there are excellent ones available from Poona, India. Various sites in Mexico are producing a variety of attractive crystals groups. Apatite, adamite, hemimorphite, aurichalcite, especially from Durango and Chihuahua provinces of Mexico are among the most attractive of current choices. Stocks of any of these are variable, and the best way to be in touch with new minerals is to keep an eye on the magazine advertisements and rockshops for new consignments.

Museum collections

One of the most enjoyable ways of pursuing this hobby is by visiting a museum collection. Most museums in mining areas, even small ones, have some sort of collection of the local minerals. The larger ones will normally have their general collection based on chemical grouping, taken from specimens embracing the widest possible distribution. In the mineral gallery in one of the great museums you can expect to find examples of all the old classics and most of the new ones. The British Museum (Natural History) in South Kensington, London, is certainly one of these, and the introductory cases explaining the subject are worth a dozen books. Most of our colour photographs, and many of those in black and white, were taken from specimens in this museum, and among them are some of the most exceptional individuals to be found anywhere.

Chalcophyllite, a rare copper arsenate, from Cornwall, in the Rashleigh collection, (see the drawing on page 138).

Scorodite, a rare iron arsenate, from Cabrestante mine, Mexico, with particularly handsome greenish-blue crystals.

Two new minerals, brown cherbetite on yellow francevilleite, from Gabon.

Drawing of chalcophyllite from Rashleigh's Specimens of British Minerals *(1797). See the original illustrated in colour on page 136.*

Above *Aragonite pseudo-hexagonal crystals from Morocco. Compare with the specimen opposite.*

*Three gypsum sand roses, from Mexico **above**, the Sahara **right**, and Kent, England **opposite page**.*

Top *A modern classic, dolomite and hemimorphite, from Sta. Eulalia, Mexico.*

Above *Aragonite crystal from the original location, Aragon, Spain. The 'hexagonal' form results from twinning.*

Crystals under the microscope. **Below** *Aurichalcite from Matlock, Derbyshire.* **Below right** *Rectangular wulfenite on tiny willemite crystals from Shah Millé, Iran.* **Bottom** *Cubes of pale fluorite with dark green crystals of olivenite from Wolfach, in the Black Forest.*

140

Below *Hexagonal mimetite on blue chrysocolla from Shah Millé, Iran.* **Bottom** *Annabergite, variant cabreite (nickel arsenate). Very rare from Lavrion, Greece.*

Of course, a visit to a museum such as this one, or to the Geological Museum, South Kensington, London, or the American Museum of Natural History in New York, or the Smithsonian Institution in Washington, DC, can be a pretty deflating experience for anyone who has been trying to put together some kind of collection of their own. Case after case of the most gorgeous specimens, the like of which are not to be found in even the most exclusive rockshop, are there to be gloated over. These are the fruits of several generations of collectors' and philanthropists' work. While museums are usually able to make occasional purchases in order to keep their collections up to date, they must work to a budget. This means that the bulk of their best specimens must come from bequests and donations. Fortunately for the general public, there have been many such public-spirited people whose enthusiasm for minerals can be shared by us all.

Not all museum specimens are so exclusive, of course, and it is often amongst the more modest ones, being closer to our own experience of them, that we can learn most about mineral recognition. In small museums, however, one must beware of errors in labelling. They do not have the budget for a specialist curator, and if they do, he will usually be very overworked. Another thing to be learnt from a good collection is the wide variety of colours and forms assumed by many minerals. Calcite is an excellent example of this. Although always crystallizing within the framework of the hexagonal system, these crystals may take the most bewildering liberties with the system and even end up with results which seem to require gymnastics in geometry to explain. While others in the same system, such as beryl, rarely seem to stray from the standard six-sided prism.

Reading
Much as you can learn from a study of the contents of museum cases, you must still turn to books for filling in the details of your knowledge. A short selection of various kinds of useful publications for the novice appears on page 143.

If you live in an area which is not well served with mineral clubs, you often have to do your own research. I have described how I ran into this problem on my return to live in England. Although there were plenty of lone collectors wandering around Cornwall whom one ran into from time to time there, was no co-ordination of their information. The Royal Geological Society of Cornwall was in the doldrums, but in their library was a large collection of the Society's transactions, as well as those of other societies, and a copy of J. H. Collins' classic study of the mineralogy of Cornwall and Devon. These, and other technical and specialist writings contained many plums of information which needed plucking out of the general pudding. Often a promising site would crop up but without

adequate identification as to its exact whereabouts. This meant more research and the study of likely maps – geological maps giving the positions of mineral veins and mine sites were invaluable – and in this way I discovered an interesting offshoot of the hobby: rockhunting in libraries. Through books you can often discover interesting sites under your very nose that are not mentioned in the usual guides.

The importance of magazines has already been mentioned. Outside North America, where periodicals of all kinds are well established, they are rather few and far between, but I have listed those most deserving of the emergent rockhound's attention.

Photographs and scale
We were lucky to be able to go to one of the world's very great collections to photograph the cream of our specimens. Certain of these are outstanding even by the exceptional standards of the British Museum. In some cases, the really remarkable feature of a mineral was not possible to convey in a photograph, that of its large size. For example wolframite is notoriously reluctant to form in good crystals. The illustration on page 80 is of a specimen which is not only very well crystallized but is about ten inches long overall. The very fine photograph of stibnite crystals on page 130 gives a good impression of size (in fact they are classics from the Japanese site at Ichinokawa), but such is the deceptiveness of the scale of minerals, that it could actually have been a much smaller group.

So if your introduction to minerals was through a museum and you embark on your first rockhunt at a site which you were told has good fluorite and galena, you may set out with visions of huge purple and silver-grey cubic crystals in mind, as on page 28. After wandering around your site for an hour, it dawns on you that you are looking for the wrong thing. The minerals are there all right, and eventually you will learn to love them, even if they are not as spellbinding as the ones you remembered in that case at the museum. What you should have been looking for are narrow fissures in certain rock, which when gently cracked open reveal a crust of small, pale straw-coloured cubes of fluorite. The galena, it turns out, is not even crystallized, and you had missed it because all the exposed specimens had acquired an inconspicuous dull grey coating. But on breaking open the right boulders they revealed attractive bands of the bright silvery cleavage faces of galena, sandwiched between alternating layers of creamy barite, as in the Sowerby illustration on page 33.

Whatever you collect and however you collect it, you will be carried along with the hobby, which increases its hold the more you get to know about it. And it is not in any sense a remote or esoteric subject, irrelevant to the real world; just the opposite, since minerals are the stuff from which everything else stems.

Reading list

Recommended books

Geology and Rocks
Principles of Geology (Nelson)
Holmes A
Well written, well illustrated

The Rock Book (Doubleday)
Fenton C L & M A
Basic information on rocks. Readable, well illustrated

Minerals
Dana's Manual of Mineralogy (Wiley)
Hurlbut C S
Good standard work. Condensed from Dana's original

Glossary of Mineral Species (Mineralogical Record).
Fleischer M
Complete list of recorded minerals with their formulas

A Field Guide to Rocks & Minerals (Constable)
Plough F H
Compact. A good basic handbook for mineral collectors

Mineralogy for Amateurs (Van Nostrand)
Sinkaukas J
A good reference work for amateurs

The Mineral Kingdom (Hamlyn)
Desautels P E
A handsome book with general appeal

Collecting and Prospecting
The Formation of Mineral Deposits (Wiley)
Bateman A M

Prospecting of Gemstones and Minerals (Van Nostrand)
Sinkaukas J
Both these books give valuable information on how to find minerals

Crystals
Crystals and Crystal Growing
Holden A & Singer P
Describing an interesting allied pursuit

Recommended periodicals

Australia
'Australian Lapidary Magazine'
Jay Kay Publications
11 Robinson Street, Croydon, New South Wales

Canada
'Canadian Rockhound'
PO Box 194, Station A, Vancouver 1, British Columbia

Great Britain
'Gems'.
The British Lapidary Magazine
29 Ludgate Hill, London EC4

USA
'Gems & Minerals'
PO Box 687, Mentone, California 92359

'Earth Science'
Earth Science Pub. Co. Inc
Mount Morris, Illinois 61054

'Lapidary Journal'
PO Box 2369, San Diego, California 92112

'Rocks & Minerals',
PO Box 29, Peekshill
NY 10566

Specifically for mineral collectors
'Mineralogical Record'
PO Box 783, Bowie, Maryland 20715

Botryoidal prehnite in basalt, from Boylestown quarry, near Glasgow, Scotland. This is a widespread mineral, often associated with zeolites.